Carbon Civilisation
and the Energy Descent Future
Life Beyond this Brief Anomaly

Samuel Alexander and Joshua Floyd

Carbon Civilisation and the Energy Descent Future
Life Beyond this Brief Anomaly

Published by the Simplicity Institute, Melbourne, in association with The Rescope Project, 2018

www.simplicityinstitute.org
www.rescopeproject.org.au

Cover image by Pawel Kuczynski © 2018

Cover design by Sharon France © 2018

Layout and typesetting by Sharon France (Looking Glass Press)

Typeset by in Hammersmith One and Stone Sans

ISBN: 978-0-9942828-0-4 (paperback ISBN)

For Laurie, Orlando and Asher, whose generation has the possibility to learn from childhood how to navigate viable energy descent pathways.

Contents

Acknowledgements

We wish to thank Damon Honnery, Patrick Moriarty, Jonathan Rutherford, Susan Krumdieck and Manfred Lenzen for providing very helpful critical feedback and comments on drafts of the book that prompted clarification of the ideas and significantly influenced its final form. We are very grateful for their advice and input. We hope to have adequately responded to the astute criticism shared in feedback, but in places there may still be points of contention. May the conversation continue! Sam would like to express thanks to the Melbourne Sustainable Society Institute for the ongoing support of his research and writing.

John Floyd provided invaluable comments on the book's structure, format and the expression of a number of key ideas, and also assisted with indexing. This, in addition to very generous support of the book's production, has helped greatly to shape and enhance the quality of the volume you now hold. We would also like to thank Sharon France for typesetting the book and designing the cover, with special thanks to Pawel Kuczynski for granting permission to use his artwork on the cover. Finally, thanks to Antoinette Wilson for proofreading.

Abbreviations

BCE   Before the Common Era

BECCS Biomass energy carbon capture and storage

CCS   Carbon capture and storage

CO₂   Carbon dioxide

EIA   U.S. Energy Information Administration

EROI   Energy return on energy investment

EV   Electric vehicle

Gbpa   Giga (billion) barrels per year

GDP   Gross domestic product

GHG   Greenhouse gas

Gt   Giga (billion) tonnes

IEA   International Energy Agency

IMF   International Monetary Fund

IPCC   Intergovernmental Panel on Climate Change

Mbpd   Mega (million) barrels per day

NETs   Negative emissions technologies

OECD   Organisation for Economic Co-operation and Development

OPEC   Organization of the Petroleum Exporting Countries

PV   Photovoltaic

RE   Renewable energy

TPES   Total primary energy supply

Chapter I. Introduction

Just as the bird's nest, the badger's lodge and the bees' hive require investments of energy for their construction and maintenance, so too with human settlements. Taken to the extremes of scale and intricacy, settlements in the form of cities constitute humanity's most energy-intensive creations. In fact, cities might be viewed as meta-creations that enable the emergence and development of other expressions of human creativity, and this creativity, as with all life, depends on energy, in requisite forms and quantities, for its sustenance and development.

A hunger for energy is woven particularly deeply into the nature and condition of modern humanity. We fell the forests and mine the landscapes to construct our dwellings and build our roads. In much of the world, heating of houses and water relies on combustion of wood, gas, oil or coal. Electricity, like a god, gives us light and it powers our abundance of convenient appliances and machines. Oil takes us where we desire to be and back again without effort. The expansion of energy harvesting and use that allows large-scale societies to grow inevitably generates new problems that these societies must then deal with. In turn, responses to such problems typically drive further energy demand. The processes by which large-scale societies take form and evolve are both enabled and constrained by their energetic foundations.

Throughout history the *over*-use of energy has not been a prevailing problem—more often, the existential challenges that humans have faced can be viewed in terms of energy *scarcity*. Had ready access to new energy sources been available, many past societies may have overcome (or at least delayed) crises that precipitated their demise.

Even so, the provision and use of energy in previous eras caused problems too. Deforestation is not a purely modern phenomenon. The harm caused by airborne particulates from burning wood and coal has a long history. As horses became a dominant mode of urban transport, their manure in the streets became a hazard. That human exploitation of energy resources should drive environmental change is not new. This is as old as the mastery of fire, and our energy use always has and always will have consequences beyond the benefits it brings.

Nevertheless, it seems that we have now entered an age in which problems that can be characterised in terms of the *under*-use of energy are being eclipsed by dilemmas in which *over*-use is central. Granted, humans enjoy vastly disparate access to energy, with billions still living in conditions of energy poverty. Collectively though, we now face dual energy crises that are distinct but intimately connected: first, fossil energy depletion, and secondly, the major contribution that combustion of these same energy sources makes to climate change. Both arise from the vastly increased scale of humanity's energy use during the industrial age. As humanity's demand for energy expands, the problems attending satisfaction of this demand intensify. To the extent that conventional responses to this situation themselves stand to further increase energy demand—including the default reliance on 'technological fixes'—the dual crises perpetuate themselves. This is the energy paradox that is coming to define our age: we expect to solve the dual energy crises with approaches that themselves demand more overall energy use.

Energy forecasting conducted within the auspices of conventional institutions typically reinforces the orthodox assumption that humanity (or the portion living in the rich world, at least) will always be able to satisfy ongoing energy demand in a timely and affordable fashion.[1] This is not necessarily a conscious assumption. Rather, it is a consequence of the ways in which large-scale societies are constituted that the association between institutional responses to collective problems and increased demand for energy is rarely apparent. As citizens of societies organised by industrial economies and market capitalism, we have simply become accustomed to overcoming (or at least displacing) any immediate problem that arises and, simultaneously, to satisfying the aggregate growth in energy demand. In mainstream energy discourse the fact that fossil fuels are finite and being depleted at pace is generally dismissed as a distant concern that will be solved before it arrives. Even if such a view is by no means universal, media narratives both reflect and propagate the widespread and popular assumption that renewable energy or nuclear power will be able to replace current fossil fuel use without significant social or economic disruption, as well as match growing global energy demand into the distant future.

In support of this energy optimism, analysts point to promising advances in technology. Sure, they say, new energy demands will arise, but a clever and resourceful humanity will be able to meet them. Markets and price signals will provide the right incentives. According to this narrative, industrial capitalism will soon be global—a transition almost complete—and efficiency gains and new energy sources and conversion technologies will mean we can avoid the worst oil depletion and climate change scenarios. Just look to history and you will see that in recent periods, humans have always managed to satisfy growing energy demand. The future will be the same, won't it?

This book challenges that dominant energy narrative from a range of angles and offers an alternative perspective on humanity's energy futures. First, we remind the reader that fossil fuels—currently comprising about 86% of global primary energy use[2] —are finite, and therefore carbon civilisation, one way or another, has a time limit. Our one-off fossil energy inheritance is but a brief anomaly in the evolution of the human story, a momentary energy spike from the perspective of deep time.

Although the timing and trajectory of fossil energy depletion is subject to many uncertainties and controversies—some of which are reviewed here—the fact that fossil fuels are finite and subject to depletion is an undeniable geological reality. This is a matter of particular significance in relation to oil, given its role in enabling industrial agriculture, and global transport systems and supply chains. With each passing day, as the low-hanging fruit is picked, it becomes harder to increase or even maintain current net energy supply. In recent years, the large growth in United States oil production due to shale oil developments using hydraulic fracturing ('fracking') techniques has encouraged some commentators to proclaim 'the death of peak oil'. Our assessment of the evidence suggests that such pronouncements are greatly exaggerated.[3] Eventually—perhaps sooner than most think—the rate of oil production will enter a phase of net energy decline, with new discoveries unable to offset the flagging fortunes of existing assets. And while oil has commanded the vast majority of attention to date in public discourse about fossil energy resource depletion, the timelines for gas and coal may not be anywhere near as protracted as is typically assumed. Alongside this, as we'll discuss in more detail as we proceed, exponential growth trends (both energetic and economic) that have defined dominant conceptions of human development since the industrial revolution can be expected to end, and even reverse. This raises questions not only about what a post-carbon civilisation will look like, but, perhaps more pressingly, how we should best manage the inevitable and foreseeable contraction of fossil energy source production in coming years and decades.

Secondly, and perhaps most prominently, there is the climate crisis, no longer of the future but the present. What was only a few years ago thought to be a sufficiently distant concern to be deferred or ignored, is now upon us. Compounding the challenge of maintaining energy supply in the face of fossil energy depletion, climate science overwhelmingly concludes that the burning of fossil fuels is a leading cause of anthropogenic climate change. Any adequate response to this potentially existential threat is going to require, among other things, a swift and committed transition beyond fossil energy sources. The best available science tells us that to keep the impacts of climate change within the range of human adaptation, we need to limit the consumption of fossil fuels even before limits are geologically enforced—that we must leave them before they leave us. The question is whether we are able to muster the wisdom to do this, and what the resultant societies might look like if we succeed. If we fail, then it seems that we will burn—and already things are heating up. According to NASA, seventeen of the eighteen hottest years in recorded history have occurred since 2001, to say nothing of the increasing regularity and severity of extreme weather events.[4] And yet we wait.

In light of the urgent imperative to reduce carbon-based fuel combustion to mitigate climate change, it may be tempting to see the prospect of fossil energy depletion as a red herring. If fossil fuel use is incompatible with maintaining a habitable climate anyway, then why be concerned about geophysical supply constraints? Surely these must, if they come into play in time, only help with the climate imperative for decarbonising economies.

While that perspective makes sense if current fossil energy reliance is viewed in very abstract terms, it oversimplifies the complex relationship between climate change and energy resource depletion.[5] The arrival of peak oil, if planned for, will unfold very differently than if it arrives without any or much preparation. So an assumption that peak oil will necessarily be good for climate change mitigation is by no means self-evident. Furthermore, in our more pessimistic moods, the sluggish political and cultural responses to climate change to date make it plausible that peak oil transforms (or disrupts) the global economy before any serious climate response does. Accordingly, it is not enough to say we *need* to decarbonise the global economy to mitigate climate change. That may be true, but if, in fact, the world fails to mobilise adequately in that regard—which, again, strikes us as a plausible scenario—then peak oil may be the energy challenge the world is *forced* to deal with.

The review of humanity's situation through the overlapping contextual lenses of fossil energy resource depletion and climate disruption sets the scene for a third context of inquiry. This concerns the extent to which alternative energy sources—specifically renewable and/ or nuclear energy—will be able to replace the fossil energy sources of carbon civilisation. Can this be achieved without significant disruption or fundamental change to its industrial, energy-intensive, extractivist and expansionary nature? We acknowledge a range of promising technological and economic advances in the energy domain, and categorically support the planned transition to a post-carbon society. At the same time, we raise critical questions about whether alternative sources can seamlessly substitute for incumbent energy systems, without transformation of the wider social and cultural contexts within which they are deployed.

Adding further to the scope of the challenge confronted in this book is the perennial question of 'who benefits?' Throughout the analysis we raise distributive questions about how the energy humanity manages to harness should be shared amongst the growing global human population, currently at 7.6 billion and, according to the United Nations, trending toward 11 billion or more by the end of the century. This is the ethical dimension that energy transition inquiries too often marginalise or simply ignore altogether, in favour of technological and market-driven solutions.

The alternative energy narrative we present maintains that we should be preparing for futures not of energy abundance, but rather of reduced energy availability, futures in which viable ways of life are characterised by energy sufficiency. With respect to the most energy intensive societies, this means planning for what permaculture theorist and practitioner David Holmgren calls 'energy descent'. While acknowledging a range of uncertainties about how humanity's energy futures will unfold, we argue that the plausibility and even the likelihood of energy descent futures implies that planning and preparing for such futures is the most prudent course of action.

The implications of this alternative narrative are profound, yet rarely addressed in the dominant discourses around energy. Our goal presently is to broaden the discourse on energy futures. If we cannot always provide comprehensive answers in the space available, we hope at least to provoke thought about new questions, with the aim of unsettling some assumptions about energy futures presently held with undue confidence. Such an act of unsettling can prepare the way for developing perspectives on energy futures that better equip humanity to find viable pathways amongst the landscape of emerging global challenges.

Chapter 2. The Role of Energy in Civilisations

It is not necessary to resort to energy determinism or crude reductionism to insist on the fundamental role energy has played, and continues to play, in shaping the rise (and demise) of human civilisations. Energy is not just another resource or commodity: it is the key that unlocks access to all other resources and commodities, thereby giving shape to the physical boundaries within which human societies must take form. A society's energetic foundations delimit the socio-economic forms that it may take. This is simply to concede that a particular form of society cannot emerge without sufficient energy supplies, in the appropriate forms, to support it. And further, that a society must be able to meet its *ongoing* energy demands if its specific socio-economic form is to persist. If it cannot, the society will transform or be transformed, voluntarily or otherwise. This chapter provides an outline of energy's defining role in human civilisations and of how expanding energy supplies have enabled the processes of socio-political complexification—increasing social role differentiation and specialisation, and expansion of the mechanisms for their coordination—typical of large-scale societies. This provides theoretical groundwork for later discussions concerning the potential socio-economic implications of energy descent.

2.1 Energy in hunter-gatherer societies

We begin in pre-history, prior to permanent human settlements, in the Palaeolithic age of the nomadic hunter-gatherers. When looking through the lens of energy, it becomes clear why and how these tribal societies were fundamentally shaped by the limited energy sources to which they had access. There are subtle lessons here relevant for us today.

Palaeolithic societies relied on direct energy from the sun for warmth and photosynthesis, which provided the energetic conditions that supported the plants and animals required for human sustenance. In time these tribes of hunter-gatherers mastered the use of fire, burning wood as fuel, reshaping societies further by extending the useful hours of the day beyond sunset, and expanding the realm of human viability into regions that were otherwise too cold to survive. But first and foremost, these early human societies were shaped by the mode in which they sourced their foundational energy supply: that is, by hunting and gathering the food needed for biophysical subsistence.

Unpacking the relationship between energy supply and socio-economic form in hunter-gatherer societies can be instructive. While some of these early societies may have been fortunate enough to emerge in conditions of such natural abundance that it was not necessary to be constantly mobile, anthropologists consider this the exception rather than the rule. Hunter-gather societies were generally nomadic societies because to subsist they needed to move wherever the food supply was most reliable. If food in a particular bioregion became scarce due to over-harvesting or some environmental determinant (e.g. drought), tribes would need to move to another bioregion in search of alternative food sources—or perish. Nevertheless, in a world relatively empty of humans, there was always a new frontier to exploit as the old one regenerated, and for hundreds of thousands of years early human societies wandered the earth in this fashion.

Note how these Palaeolithic societies were generally nomadic by force of context and circumstance. Often it was the most expedient means at hand to secure the food—that is, the energy supply— needed for basic subsistence. Note further how other socio-economic consequences flowed from being nomadic. There were powerful incentives not to build permanent, labour-intensive dwellings if the tribe needed to relocate between bioregions periodically in order to secure a continuous food supply. It appears that hunting and gathering were capable of delivering sufficient relative energy surpluses per unit of labour to allow groups to meet their biophysical needs with abundant leisure time. This was possible by working within the biophysical productivity limits of the landscape—that is, labour productivity could remain high, provided excessive pressure was not exerted on the 'natural' productivity of the land. In this situation, any attempt to increase the absolute energy surplus by applying more labour would push the land towards its productivity limit, hence reducing labour's marginal return. As long as a tribe's demands on the environment remained relatively modest, a modest amount of labour could comfortably meet the needs of its way of life. But satisfying demands beyond this level would become increasingly onerous. By the same token, having modest demands that could be met by means that left ample time available for play acted as a disincentive against working harder in order to achieve increased absolute surpluses. And this carried with it the attendant benefit that large-scale institutions and infrastructures, which would *require* these large energy surpluses for their provision and maintenance, were rendered unnecessary.

Moreover, the need for nomadic tribes to carry possessions with them in search of the next meal provided a compelling practical reason to maintain only tools of exceptional value. Not only would further possessions be an encumbrance requiring more energy in the form of food to transport them, natural predators and rival tribes provided an incentive to travel as lightly as possible in order to fight or flee more effectively. If the desire for possessions was limited in the first place, and if insufficient absolute energy surplus was available to support the development and transportation even of those that were desired, then socio-economic forms suited to providing them would not emerge.

Although this picture of the Palaeolithic era is painted only in the broadest brushstrokes, it serves the purpose of highlighting how the limited energy sources available to pre-historic societies (that is, sources made available by biophysical processes that were influenced relatively modestly by human activity compared with the subsequent Neolithic situation) shaped their nature and strongly delimited the potential for socio-political complexification. Societies were about as 'simple' (in the limited social scientific sense) as can be imagined.[6]

2.2 Agriculture, energy surplus and socio-political complexification

The development or 'discovery' of agriculture and animal husbandry in the Neolithic era, circa 10,000 BCE, marked a major branch point in the social evolution of *homo sapiens*. In fact, this is the point typically recognised as the 'birth of civilisation'. Securing sufficient food for human subsistence was less dependent on the natural supply provided by local ecosystems and more so on active planning and management of food production systems (i.e. cultivating soils, planting, managing the water cycle, and later harvesting crops) oriented towards the provision of storable surpluses.

Although it was not always an abrupt or immediate transition, the move to agriculture gave humans more control over their food supply—a Promethean step, it would seem, in our ongoing efforts to force nature to serve our own purposes rather than adjust ourselves to nature's rhythms and vicissitudes. What is more, the very nature of agriculture implied that such societies had to become sedentary, in order to reap where they had sown. Thus agriculture provided the incentive to give up nomadic ways of life and create permanent settlements—first the village, then the town, and eventually the city. It could perhaps be said that contemporary industrial societies are but footnotes to this disruptive Neolithic innovation.

The uptake of agriculture can be understood to be as much a revolution in energy supply as a revolution in the mode of sourcing food. It provided human societies with an absolute energy surplus that both enabled *and* necessitated a process of socio-political complexification that we are still experiencing today. We are products of this process as well as participants in it. Soon after its inception, agriculture came to be far more productive per acre than hunting and gathering, and the exploitation of animals (for food and labour) provided a further energy boost. This meant that agricultural societies were able to support the growing proportion of what are sometimes called 'non-food specialists' that such societies required in order to support and enable their large scale.[7]

With only a portion of an agricultural population working as farmers in order to feed their society, the remainder of the population had more time (and energy) to do other things. This included developing technologies, tools, and weapons; establishing an army or church; making art; or administering, coordinating, and governing the expanding activities of agricultural society. The increased productivity of agriculture (per acre, rather than per hour of labour) also significantly increased the overall food supply, such that a growing population could be supported in a given bioregion to an extent not viable with hunting and gathering alone.[8] This came at the cost, however, of a larger number of agricultural workers in absolute terms working longer hours than in Palaeolithic societies—that is, the labour cost per unit of food produced was higher.

In societies that were now sedentary, investing time and energy in building labour-intensive permanent dwellings came to be seen as worthwhile and economically feasible—the benefits of this outweighed the costs. This signifies a shift in balance that eventuated with time in the city's birth as a locus for creative human endeavour. Permanent dwellings also became necessary as populations were anchored by the infrastructures required to enable their ways of life, all of which required ongoing development and maintenance. As forests were depleted, the means of building temporary shelters was also lost, and the nature of the materials available for shelter construction (stone, mud, etc.) necessitated long-term investment in fixed structures.

The sedentary nature of agricultural societies also provided the conditions for *accumulation* (of possessions, tools, land, etc.) to an extent that was prohibitive or simply unthinkable when living nomadically. Conflict over land and possessions arose, precipitating early forms of customary property rights and rules, which in turn needed rudimentary mechanisms of enforcement, protection, and interpretation. Thus agriculture can be understood as the original driver for the emergence of political societies themselves and the various institutions of government such societies require. In short, human societies started becoming significantly more complex in social scientific terms—the available energy surplus was able to fund a greater diversity of social roles, technologies, bureaucracies, and institutions.

Notably, the viability of an army and the development of more effective weapons also produced new power relations between rival human groups. Agricultural societies had a great power advantage over hunter-gatherer societies and thus were generally able to expand their territories as necessary, violently or otherwise. For better or for worse, this new militaristic power that flowed from the energy surplus provided by agriculture had clear evolutionary advantages: societies that did not adopt agriculture were vulnerable to being overpowered by other societies that did. It should come as no surprise then that the vast majority of people alive today live in societies dependent on agriculture. As these societies continue to expand their territories, the viability of hunter-gatherer existence decreases by the day. We see here a compelling reason for societies to seek absolute energy surpluses through agriculture in order to support ongoing socio-political complexification: do so not because you necessarily want to, but because if you do not, your way of life will be stamped out of existence.

Again, the analysis has been so brief that simplification has been necessary, but the essential dynamic should be clear enough: solving problems of any scale posed by human existence requires sufficient energy. Moreover, the nature of the response to the problems posed is shaped fundamentally by the energy sources available. In this light, the Neolithic adoption of agriculture is usefully conceptualised as a revolution in energy supply. The new energy supply underpinned the socio-political complexification of human societies through the nature and scale of the energy surplus it provided.

Maintaining that complexity required that energy supply be maintained at a sufficient rate. As further problems inevitably arose and solutions were implemented, and as further human wants were satisfied, a society's required rate of energy supply increased. This dynamic of socio-political complexification drives human hunger for energy. After all, if a society's energy supply could not meet the demands of its increasing complexity, the society's socio-economic form could not persist. The society would either have to adjust to reduced energy supply and embrace voluntary simplification[9] —a strategy we consider in later chapters—or else deteriorate and eventually collapse as more problems arose for which the society lacked sufficient energy surplus to solve.[10]

These pre-industrial agricultural societies had various energy sources that funded their growing complexity: wood (and later coal) combustion for heating dwellings, cooking, and smelting, refining and working metals; food to sustain human and animal labour; wind to power sailing vessels and eventually windmills; and water flowing under gravity was distributed via aqueducts and used to power water wheels. All these contributed to the energy surpluses needed to support growing socio-political complexity, with Roman civilisation providing a prime historical example. But combined, these energy sources pale in comparison with the energy surpluses that humanity (or parts at least) began to exploit from the middle of the 18th century, funding a degree of socio-political complexification hitherto unimaginable.

2.3 Fossil fuels, industrialisation and the birth of carbon civilisation

If agriculture was the first true revolution in energy supply that humanity experienced, the second accompanied the wave of industrial revolutions starting in 18th-century England. These led directly to the harnessing of the vast energy potential associated with the fossil fuels: coal, then oil, and later natural gas. The technological and economic explosion that began with the invention and refinement of the steam engine changed the fundamentals of how humans (in the industrialising societies at least) lived on Earth.[11] It is hard to overstate the significance of this energy revolution and yet so easy to take it for granted, not just in terms of the *magnitude* of energy now available but also the *nature* of that energy.

Regarding magnitude, the point is made most emphatically with respect to oil, one barrel (or 159 litres) of which can enable a quantity of work equivalent to something in the order of three years of human labour.[12] And in 2017 global oil production reached over 95 million barrels per day.[13] The figure is so astonishing that it really does deserve repeating: a single barrel of oil can enable work equivalent to three years of human labour, and currently humanity uses over 95 million barrels *every day*—or 33 billion barrels per year. In the absence of fossil fuels, an average citizen of a typical industrially advanced society today would need the human labour of between 50 and 90 'energy slaves' working in eight-hour shifts seven days a week, year on year, in order to meet the aggregate energy demand of their energy intensive way of life.[14] To deliver the work equivalent of current world total primary energy demand would require over *170 billion* such 'energy slaves'. Pause for a moment to let those figures sink in.

But the magnitude of energy supplied by fossil fuels is only part of the story. Their unique *nature* is no less extraordinary. The significance of this is even easier to take for granted—or to miss altogether. This can perhaps be illustrated most clearly with respect to the concept of 'power density'—the *rate* at which energy can be supplied and used *per spatial unit*, such as volume or land area. Returning to the previous example, it is not just the quantity of energy available from each barrel that makes oil such an extraordinary energy source; the further feature which sets it (along with coal and gas) apart from other energy sources is the *very high rate* at which that energy can be used *in a relatively small space*.

The very high power densities enabled by fossil fuels play a key role in the high aggregate rates at which energy services can be provided. The energy equivalent to three years' worth of human labour that a barrel of oil provides can be exploited in a fraction of that time. As a result, activities or practices that would simply not be possible in the absence of such energy sources become available, such as high-speed air travel, extreme urban densification and mining for resources thousands of metres below the earth's surface. Industrial societies can do things that were impossible in pre-industrial societies. Even if those earlier societies had all the horses and windmills they needed to provide the total energy inputs for such practices, the power densities of those energy sources were insufficient for bringing about the types of physical change that we now take for granted. Scale of physical change is one thing; the rate and spatial intensity at which it is effected is another—and in each regard the accomplishments enabled by fossil fuels are utterly unique.

In addition to the power densities that they enable, the ease with which fossil fuels can be stored and transported sets them apart from most other energy sources. It is difficult to capture energy from the sun or wind for later or distant use. But fossil fuels are ready and waiting when needed, in forms that can be easily captured, stored, and transported. Add to those remarkable characteristics the virtues of cheapness (at least when externalities are excluded) and historical abundance, and it becomes clearer how and why fossil fuels have shaped—both in terms of the magnitude *and* nature of the energy surplus they provide—the socio-political and economic characteristics of what we call here *carbon civilisation*.

At this stage we could consider the image of the metropolis at night, as seen from an aeroplane window, to highlight the practical implications of this energy analysis. The aircraft itself is entirely dependent on the unique power density of oil, not simply to provide the fuel, but also to make viable the range of complex background activities on which modern aircraft depend: the mining of materials and the production of plastics; the laying of roads and runways; the development and production of computers and communications technologies that coordinate the tens of thousands of daily flights; to say nothing of the broader investment in education required to train the engineers, computer scientists, pilots, and so forth. In this web of dependencies it is not long before one arrives at the combine harvester that plays a key role in feeding much of the population. These machines, also powered by oil, take the Neolithic innovation of freeing up human labour for 'non-food specialisation' and amplify its effects through the industrialisation of agriculture. If in the past essentially all members of hunter-gatherer societies were required to be 'food specialists', in some industrially advanced societies today the proportion of the population required to be farmers has dropped to as low as 2%.[15] During this demographic transition people were displaced from the land by machines and into the factories and offices of the built environment. It is this image of mass migration that perhaps most vividly illustrates the tight interrelationship between intensification of socio-political complexity and the urbanisation of modern life in the industrialised world.

Beneath the aircraft lie the sprawling, glowing suburbs—the defining manifestation of carbon civilisation on the ground. No previous form of human settlement has ever been more energy intensive to produce or to maintain. Again, think through the long and diverse chains of extraction and production on which suburbia depends, not only for its creation but also to support the high-consumption ways of life widely practised there: the underlying energy infrastructure like oil and gas pipelines and the electricity grid; the mining and transport activities that siphon resources from the global periphery to the urban and suburban landscapes; and the final consumer commodities shipped and trucked to the shopping malls, via a vast and complex network of global trade routes and practices; the manufacture of vehicles to transport people to and from work, leisure, and tourist activities; the production of houses, kitchen gadgets, plastics, computers, pharmaceuticals, appliances, and clothing; refrigeration of food; water heating, and space heating and cooling; and, thanks to hydrocarbon-derived fertilisers, the abundant provision of food from all around the world, no matter the season, free from blemishes due to the liberal use of hydrocarbon-derived pesticides and herbicides. The list really has no end, because in our increasingly globalised and interconnected world-spanning economy everything seems dependent on everything else. Nothing, though, is more fundamental than the fossil fuels that make other physical transformation possible. Just look around the space in which you are reading: it may not always be obvious, but essentially every artefact you see will have a history saturated with fossil energy, especially oil.

This is carbon civilisation.

Chapter 3. Carbon Civilisation, Economic Growth and the Finitude of Fossil Fuels

The analysis so far highlights the ways in which carbon civilisation has been enabled by the vast and unprecedented energy surpluses provided by fossil fuels. This is apparent in the close correlation between world gross domestic product (GDP) and total primary energy use, shown for the period 1965–2016 in Figure 1. This tight relationship draws attention to the dependence that all economic activity has on physical transformations, and hence on the energy services—work, heating, illumination—necessary to effect these transformations. Figure 2 shows the sharply increasing energy supply required to enable the unprecedented growth and industrialisation of economies over the last two centuries. Our globalised modes of production, distribution and consumption simply would not have been possible without the energy surpluses provided by fossil fuels. Figure 3 makes clear how the vast majority of energy supply growth has come from fossil fuels. It shows also the extent of the continued reliance on these energy sources.

However, there is only a limited amount of fossil fuels in the ground and in the last two centuries humanity has been extracting these historically cheap, seemingly abundant, but ultimately finite resources with ravenous enthusiasm. This raises questions about what may happen as these non-renewable energy sources continue to deplete in coming years and decades. It is this issue to which we now turn, focusing primarily on the problem of oil dependency in the face of such depletion. At the same time, we acknowledge that there is some scope for substitution between oil, gas and coal, and so the trajectories and consequences of fossil fuel depletion will necessarily be more complex than a focus on oil, independent of coal and gas, can provide.

We provide some further brief commentary on the interrelationships between oil, coal and gas depletion in an endnote.[16]

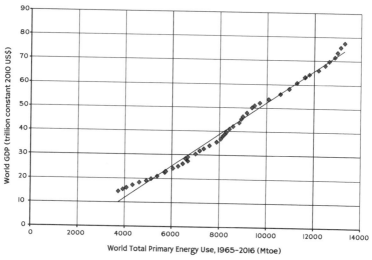

Figure 1: World GDP versus total primary energy use, for the period 1965–2016. The strong correlation between GDP and energy use is apparent, with $R^2 = 0.9907$ for the linear trend line shown ($y = 0.0067x - 14.935$). Data sources: world GDP, World Bank; energy use, BP Statistical Review of World Energy 2017.

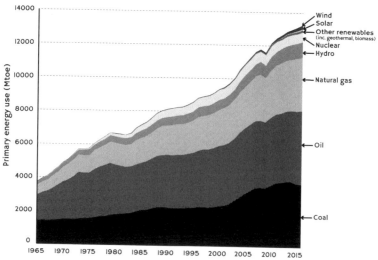

Figure 2: Time series of absolute world total primary energy use by source 1965–2016, indicating the dominant role of fossil fuels. Data source: BP Statistical Review of World Energy June 2017.

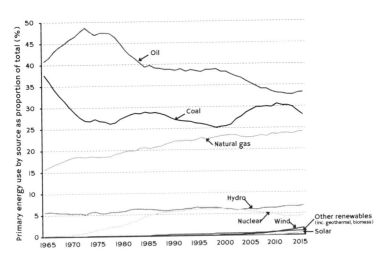

Figure 3: Time series of relative share of world total primary energy use by source 1965–2016, indicating the dominant role of fossil fuels. Data source: BP Statistical Review of World Energy June 2017.

3.1 Peak oil and the economic implications of rising energy costs

Throughout most of the 20th century, oil supply was able to meet increasing demand without much trouble. Leaving aside the geopolitical oil crises of 1973 and 1979, cheap oil in the range of $20–25 per barrel was readily available. Naturally, industrial economies came to rely on these cheap energy inputs and structured their societies accordingly, assuming energy costs would continue to account for a relatively minor fraction of overall production inputs and that economic growth trajectories could be maintained indefinitely. Around 2005, however, conventional crude oil production stagnated due to geological constraints[17] and the theory of 'peak oil' began to be taken seriously within mainstream institutions.

Peak oil refers to the point in time where oil production (for a given territory, ranging from a single field to the global aggregate) reaches its maximum rate. This point arrives not because oil is 'running out' as such but because most of the 'low-hanging fruit' (the easy-to-produce oil) has already been discovered and extracted, leaving increasingly marginal oil reserves as the focus for future production development (e.g deep water or arctic oil, tar sands and shale oil). These marginal reserves are costlier to extract, both financially and energetically. As conventional oil depletes, producers have to run faster and faster—or drill ever-more wells, in ever-less-favourable places—merely to maintain overall production at a constant level. Like any resource, the process of extracting oil has diminishing marginal returns (though technology improvement can reduce the rate at which returns diminish). Eventually oil producers will not be able to maintain supply rates, however hard they try, and the flow of oil will stop growing, or 'peak', and subsequently fall. This can be expected, despite the fact there will still be considerable quantities of oil left to produce—in fact, according to peak oil theory, about half of all oil that will ever be recovered. This is not a geological phenomenon in isolation. In ways outlined below, geology and economics (plus geopolitics) become intertwined in a complex interrelationship, with mutually influencing factors giving shape to the rise, peak and decline of oil supply. On top of this, culture and technology also shape the interplay between demand and production rates.

The peak oil school is primarily concerned with the consequences of the peak and decline of global oil production arriving while demand for oil is still growing. Basic market principles dictate that a constrained supply coupled with increasing demand will drive rapid increase in oil prices. Given how much oil is used today, and given the constraints on substituting other energy sources for it, expensive oil places a huge financial burden on oil-dependent economies, with destabilising effects.[18] As conventional oil production began to plateau around 2005, and global demand continued to increase, the price of oil commenced a steady incline, moving from its historic average of $20–25 per barrel (where it sat even in the late 20th century) to over $100 by 2008. This basic dynamic played out essentially as the peak oil school predicted, even if the interplay between geology, economics, technology, culture and geopolitics proved to be more complicated and nuanced than petroleum geologists and other analysts anticipated. Today conventional crude oil production remains on what is often described as an 'undulating plateau', a phenomenon acknowledged by mainstream institutions including the International Energy Agency (IEA). In other words, conventional crude oil seems to have peaked. Any gains from now on, if they occur, will be negligible.

Nevertheless, as the production rate for conventional oil stopped growing, the consequent price rise made various unconventional petroleum resources more economically viable. This facilitated their production by incentivising the deployment and development of suitable recovery technologies (including 'fracking' techniques). This meant that global oil supply from all sources was able to keep up with growing global demand, delaying a peak in overall liquid fuels.

But meeting this growing demand came at a huge financial cost and the intimate relationship between energy and economics became more readily apparent. No longer could the cost of oil as a production input be treated as insignificant. After a century of cheap energy inputs, industrial economies (especially the oil importers) found their dependence on oil to be an increasingly debilitating financial burden.

We should be clear about the extent of this financial burden. By 2012 the global economy was using oil at the rate of around 90 million barrels per day (Mbpd). When trying to maintain consumption at such a level the difference between oil at $25 per barrel and oil priced over $100 per barrel becomes hugely significant. To be precise, it constitutes an extra cost to the global economy of around $7.2 billion dollars per day, or $3.6 trillion dollars per year—money that would otherwise have been spent in the broader economy. If we look specifically at the United States—the world's largest oil consumer—the rise in the price of oil from $25 to over $100 meant that the US was spending an extra $600 million every day on oil imports. This money was not just being sucked *into* the energy sector, but *out of* the national economy altogether.

In light of these figures, it is not difficult to understand why 10 of the last 11 recessions in the United States have been associated with high oil prices.[19] Or why the 2008 global financial implosion correlated so closely with oil prices spiking to an unprecedented level of over $140 per barrel (in July 2008).[20] When oil gets expensive, every other fundamental economic enabler dependent on oil—like transport, mechanised labour, industrial food production and plastics, amongst innumerable other inputs—gets more expensive too.

This pricing dynamic siphons discretionary expenditure and investment away from the rest of the economy—or out of the national economy altogether—causing debt defaults, economic stagnation, recessions or even longer-term depressions.[21] It would be too simplistic to argue that expensive oil was the *only* cause of the global financial crisis (and the ongoing concerns about sluggish economic growth). Nevertheless, it would be just as blind to deny the defining role expensive oil played both in the global financial crisis and the state of the sluggish global economy today.[22] Given the enormous fossil fuel inputs required for industrial agriculture, expensive oil also leads to spikes in food prices, and these in turn drive disruptive societal effects. Poorer countries are particularly vulnerable to the impact of oil prices on the cost of food.[23]

As oil becomes scarcer in coming years and decades, this energy-economy dynamic is likely to tighten its grip on oil-dependent societies. This is especially so in light of continued demand growth for this finite, non-renewable resource as more of the world industrialises. Oil demand is currently increasing each year by around 1 Mbpd. Despite hopes for a near-term 'demand peak', this ongoing demand increase is expected to continue until at least 2040.[24]

3.2 Why did the price of oil drop in mid-2014?

Standard peak oil theory informs the analysis above and coherently explains the key dynamics under examination. The situation gets more complicated and controversial, however, when trying to understand why, after the price of oil averaged over $100 from 2011 to mid-2014—suggesting a 'new normal'—the price then dropped to the $40–60 range, rising to $60–70 only in the first half of 2018. If geological constraints were making it harder to meet growing oil demand, as the peak oil school contended, shouldn't the price of oil have continued to trend upwards? Doesn't the sharp fall in price imply resource abundance, thus debunking peak oil concerns? On the basis of the price plunge, the 'death of peak oil' has been widely announced.

While the timing of this sudden drop in price indeed took energy and financial analysts by surprise, there are economic, geological and geopolitical dynamics at play in light of which the price volatility we are seeing is not actually so surprising. In fact, there are two principal factors with which we can explain the situation with a high degree of confidence, both entirely consistent with the fundamental assumptions of peak oil analysis. The first is a demand-side factor; the second, a supply-side factor. These are not mutually exclusive and in fact interactions between these factors exacerbate their respective effects, hence the fall in price being so dramatic.

The demand-side factor influencing the price drop is that growth in the global economy has stagnated relative to the period prior to 2008, a diagnosis shared by most mainstream analysts (e.g. IMF, the World Bank). This sluggish and uncertain growth is partly due to several years of historically expensive oil—averaging over $100 from 2011 to mid-2014. As we have explained, this has had a retarding effect on the expected growth trajectories of oil-dependent economies. When economic growth is strong, oil demand is high; when economies are weak, stagnant or in recession, oil demand is weak.

However, when oil demand is weaker than expected while supply is maintained, basic market principles dictate that the price of oil will fall, and this is precisely what we have seen. Another way to frame this demand-side point is to say that when oil is expensive, it becomes increasingly unaffordable, especially when wages stagnate or fall. This unaffordability induces 'demand destruction', which reduces pressure on oil supply chains. It could even be said that there is not really a glut of cheap oil so much as there is a glut of businesses and consumers that cannot afford to buy what is perceived as expensive oil. Keep in mind that even oil at $60 per barrel is still two or three times more costly than the historic average, disincentivising consumption. Consequently, reduced pressure on oil markets manifested in reduced prices. All this is perfectly comprehensible, even if the exact timing of the effects could never be predicted with any precision.

The second principal factor influencing the currently depressed prices can also be understood in relation to the prolonged period of expensive oil in recent years, but this time from the supply-side. Historically, the vast deposits of unconventional oil around the world (especially in the tar sands of Canada and Venezuela, the shale oil plays in the US and some deep water resources) have been under-exploited, because the expenditure needed to produce them has been so great that it would have been uneconomic to do so.

But the plateau in conventional oil production beginning around 2005 applied a supply-side constraint to global oil markets, inducing a steady rise in the price of oil. As the price reached beyond $100 and seemed to stabilise, it suddenly appeared as if much more of this unconventional oil could be produced for a profit. This naturally provoked something of an investment frenzy, especially in the US and Canada, resulting in the major resurgence in US oil production and the steady rise in Canadian tar sands production. Several years of manic drilling has resulted in a short-term glut in oil supply, precipitating an inevitable price fall.

It is worth highlighting the important interactions here between the demand-side and the supply-side dynamics. As we have seen, expensive oil places a burden on oil-dependent economies, making it difficult to maintain expected or desired growth trajectories, and inducing demand destruction. But just as oil demand was weakening due to poor economic performance (as conventionally measured), the very same phenomenon of expensive oil was bringing new supply chains to market. If these supply and demand dynamics were at play in isolation, they would have produced a drop in the price of oil. When they occur together—that is, when demand is being destroyed by expensive oil just as expensive oil is incentivising increased production—it should come as no surprise that at some point the markets would react. Since mid-2014 we have seen precisely that occur.

3.3 Ten reasons why preparing for scarce and expensive oil is prudent

We have outlined why the three years of $100+ oil from 2011 to mid-2014—following the plateau in conventional oil production and tightening oil markets—provided temporary relief from the impacts of peak oil. As we have set out, this reprieve occurred as high prices drove demand destruction and incentivised investment in production of unconventional sources, especially shale oil. But far from debunking the peak oil phenomenon, the current situation is a reflection of it. The most worrying implications of peak oil—including recessions, food crises or even the collapse of oil-dependent economies—should remain of concern to those who look beneath the surface of the current oil glut, so-called. Below we summarise ten key reasons why peak oil is not dead but is, at best, in temporary remission. Any one of these is sufficient to show that peak oil is on its way and remains of critical importance in thinking about humanity's futures; together they point to a looming and foreseeable energy crunch as the energy foundations of carbon civilisation deplete while demand continues to grow.

1. **Oil production in the rest of the world (excluding US and Canada) is flat.** Perhaps the most compelling evidence to remind people of the geological inevitability of peak oil is the fact that the rest of world (excluding the US and Canada) produces no more oil today than it did in 2005.[25] In 2005 the Royal Swedish

Academy of Sciences reviewed oil producers globally and concluded that 54 of the largest 65 oil producers had already peaked or were in decline, with other nations joining that group since then.[26] In 2016, an HSBC report concluded that 64–81% of world oil production is already in decline.[27]

Were it not for the 'shale boom' in the US and the slowly rising production from Canadian tar sands, global oil production probably would have peaked already. Given that future increases in Canada are expected to be small, and that the oil majors have in fact recently been selling their Canadian assets at pace, [28] it looks like future production increase is primarily reliant on the US. Saudi Arabia probably has some limited spare capacity but in coming years declines elsewhere around the world will require that capacity to come on line just for global production to remain flat, meaning that overall non-US production is likely to remain on an undulating plateau before declining.

But just as most of the rest of the world is peaking now, at some stage in the foreseeable future US production will also peak. The typically optimistic U.S. Energy Information Administration (EIA) and the IEA both presently think US production will peak in or around 2025.[29] Whether it is a few years either side, the fact of a forthcoming peak is a geological inevitability, because fossil fuels are finite and non-renewable. If demand continues to increase, as expected—suggesting that any near-term prospect of 'peak demand' is highly unlikely[30]—this will tighten oil markets and induce a sharply rising oil price that will likely have contractionary effects on oil-dependent economies, bringing an end to historic economic and energy growth trends. Peak oil, therefore, is not dead but has merely been delayed a few years because of the shale boom. The mood of complacency induced by this is worrying.

2. **Uncertainties over future US shale production.**[31] Executive Director of the IEA, Fatih Birol, states that US shale production is 'the key question for the future of the oil market'.[32] A recent

3: Carbon Civilisation, Economic Growth and the Finitude of Fossil Fuels

report by Wood Mackenzie suggests that the most productive shale plays (in the Permian Basin) could peak in 2021, which would imply an overall shale peak in the US.[33] Other analyses support this timeline.[34]

Indeed, a recent MIT study outlines reasons to doubt more optimistic projections.[35] The study's authors argue that EIA shale oil projections assume that recent production increases in the US have been due to efficiency gains from technological advances, and that the EIA extrapolates those efficiency gains into the future. But the MIT study shows that the efficiency gains have been largely due to low oil price. This has incentivised producers to extract the sweetest, low-cost spots first, and these are inherently limited. This is the real reason production has increased. That such efficiency gains will continue into coming decades is implausible because as production proceeds, the sweet spots are being depleted. The EIA has acknowledged that the MIT study makes 'some valid points' and was based on better data than it had available.[36]

Perhaps the most pressing challenge to maintaining the shale boom, however, is questionable profitability.[37] Between the oil price crash of mid-2014 and late 2017, 134 US oil production and exploration companies filed for bankruptcy.[38] It is not clear that shale oil is (or can remain) profitable with oil prices around the $60 mark, which means that in the absence of sustained price increase, a shale bust could arrive sooner than most analysts think.[39] Indeed, the *Wall Street Journal* reported in 2017 that over the preceding decade the shale oil industry in the US has spent $280 billion more on investments than it has generated from operations. How long can this capital sink continue? It is no good having vast, technically recoverable resources if producing them is uneconomic. Accordingly, if US production peaks in the next few years (for whatever reason) then global production of all oil is likely to peak as a consequence. This would signify an historic, era-defining turning point.

The world is likely to be very poorly prepared for such a turning point. The prominent US government 'Hirsch Report' of 2005 optimistically suggested that 10 to 20 years would be required to prepare a society adequately for peak oil.[40] Hirsch also notes that something like $50–100 trillion of machinery around the world was built to run on oil (not electricity). Moving away from this oil-dependent infrastructure will be slow, difficult and expensive.[41] Vaclav Smil also highlights how slowly energy systems have changed in history. So whether the global peak in oil production occurs in 2020 or 2025 is almost beside the point. It seems the world is going to be unprepared for the eventual peak in production of all liquids, even if it is still ten years away.

3. **Oil discoveries at record low and decline rates increasing.** Despite absolute demand for oil being at historic highs and continuing to increase, discoveries of oil are the lowest since 1947.[42] In 2016, the IEA reported that oil demand was over 85 Mbpd, or 31 billion barrels per year (Gbpa) (and just under 95 Mbpd or 35 Gbpa if all liquid fuels are included). Yet discoveries that year were a measly 2.4 billion barrels, much less than one tenth of what was consumed. In 2017 there were even fewer discoveries.[43] Compare this with average discoveries of 9 Gbpa over the previous 15 years.[44] The unsustainability of this situation should be obvious: if a civilisation is using ten times as much oil as it is discovering each year, there is a serious problem looming, just as there would be a serious problem if a household was spending ten times what it was earning.

But far from trying to adjust to this and rein in demand, the world is increasing its dependency on oil even as discoveries are destined to decline further due to geological scarcity. Furthermore, as noted earlier, the 2016 HSBC report concludes that 64–81% of existing fields are in decline, making it ever harder to maintain existing levels of supply. Assuming an expected decline rate of 5–7% per year, the report shows that:

the supply lost between 2016 and 2040 amounts to 41–48 Mbpd [roughly 15–18 Gbpa]. For context, this is broadly 4x [four times] the current crude oil output of OPEC's largest producer, Saudi Arabia (c.10.5 Mbpd [3.8 Gbpa]). Assuming all other pre-peak production is held constant, this is the amount needed just to keep supply flat. To provide in addition for the expected rise in global demand over the period, the additional supply needed could be closer to 55–60 Mbpd [20–22 billion Gbpa].[45]

4. **Energy-return-on-investment in terminal decline.** Discoveries in terminal decline while production from existing fields is also declining would be bad enough. Yet this is not the end of the story. The resources that *are* being discovered are becoming harder and more expensive to produce. The 'low-hanging fruit' is gone. It is often claimed in the literature that in the 1930s, oil production in the US had an energy-return-on-investment (EROI) of 100:1. That is, the oil industry could invest one barrel of oil in new production capacity and expect a return of 100 barrels at the wellhead. But as the easiest-to-produce oil was consumed, the EROI of oil inevitably declined. By the 1970s, the average EROI for global oil production had sunk to around 30:1 at the wellhead. Today the global EROI for oil is something like 17:1, and declining.[46] In the US, wellhead EROI is around 11:1, and declining. The equivalent EROI of biofuels is generally in the range of 1–3:1.[47]

As the best resources continue to be exploited first, the decline in EROI is destined to continue by virtue of physics and geology. The oil industry is therefore forced into producing resources of ever diminishing EROI, such as deep-water oil, tar sands, shale oil and biofuels. This will apply relentless upward pressure to the financial and energetic costs of production at a given production level, since these typically go up as EROI declines (potentially offset to some extent by technical developments). It is cheaper—both financially and energetically—to extract oil from a gusher in Texas than in thousands of feet of water in the Gulf of Mexico.

The key point, however, concerns 'net energy'. Declining EROI means the net energy per barrel produced reduces. Even if overall oil production is maintained at a fixed level, as EROI declines, the energy surplus available for the rest of society reduces, since increasing amounts are required by the energy sector itself. In fact, if high-EROI oil is being replaced with low-EROI oil it is possible for oil production to grow and yet for net energy available for the rest of society to decline. This would likely hide the reality of energy descent from observers who ignore the energy costs of supply. Indeed, this is why peak oil may only be accepted by most people when seen through the rear-view mirror—by which time the window for adequate response will have passed.[48]

5. **Oil industry facing major financial challenges.** The new economics of oil indicates that the heyday of the oil industry is coming to an end. Amongst the most profitable industries of the 20th century, the profitability of oil seems to be turning sharply. As the cost of finding and producing oil rises relentlessly, depressed prices render the profit expectations of the previous era obsolete.[49] Between 1998 and 2005, capital expenditure for the oil industry amounted to $1.5 trillion. Over the same period, this drove production growth of 8.6 Mbpd (3.1 Gbpa). Contrast that with the period 2005–2013 (immediately following the conventional oil peak), when capital expenditure of $4 trillion increased oil production by only 2.4 Mbpd (0.9 Gbpa).[50] That is, the industry is investing far more only to be getting a far lower return. This trend is destined to continue as EROI declines further and the remaining 'sweet spots' are depleted.

So how is all this affecting profits? In 2004 (the year before conventional oil peaked), the seven largest oil 'majors' had a combined net income of $99.2 billion. In 2016, that figure had dropped approximately 90%, to $10.5 billion.[51] That's still a lot of money, but it is the sharp downward trend that is noteworthy. And in parallel with this decline in profitability, capital expenditure by the oil majors, according to Steve Kopits, has been rising by 11% per year since 1999.[52] Debt levels tell a similar story of trouble. In 2007 the combined debt of the majors was $84 billion, yet by 2016 combined debt had risen to $379 billion.[53] All this suggests that the oil industry has entered a new era, where profits are in sharp decline while debts are skyrocketing to unprecedented levels. The oil price collapse also impacted OPEC member states deeply. According to the OPEC Secretary General, 'over the past two years, we saw not only a drop in investment in the sector but also a decrease in oil revenues. Collectively, OPEC countries lost more than $1 trillion.'[54]

6. **Lack of investment due to low prices.** The combined impacts of these geological and financial factors can also give rise to oil industry investment decisions that lead to the tightening of oil markets and associated price volatility. When oil was over $100 per barrel, the industry developed production sources that it is not prepared to invest in when oil is at $50–60 per barrel. Even when oil is physically available 'in the ground', it may not be brought to market in a timely fashion due to the delay between initial investment decisions and new production capacity coming on-line.

A study by Goldman Sachs concludes that the low oil price means that $1 trillion of oil investment funds are now at risk of being withdrawn from projects. This could reduce production by 7.5 Mbpd (2.7 Gbpa) over the coming decade.[55] In 2016, Tim Gould, head of the IEA's energy supply outlook division, said that due to low investment in oil projects it is 'increasingly unlikely that supply will be able to meet the rising demand without rapid price increases.'[56] In the same year a report from Barclays concluded that due to low investment, 2019 could see 'the lowest year for new capacity' on record, and could result in a supply gap of almost 3 Mbpd (1 Gbpa).[57] The head of Citibank thinks that the squeeze could come in 2018,[58] and rising price in the early months of 2018 arguably supports this view.

7. **Peak exports.** When thinking about oil supply, the rapidly increasing consumption *within oil exporting nations* is seldom appreciated or discussed. This rise in consumption is making it more difficult for those nations to maintain existing export levels. As consumption grows within oil exporting nations, and as production growth stagnates, there is a great incentive for those nations to keep more oil for themselves. It follows that the OECD nations, for example, should not assume that in future they will receive the same proportion of global oil production as they do presently.[59]

Indeed, as a result of the peak in conventional oil production, exports also seem to have peaked around 2006–7.[60] Since domestic production by most importers is also declining, this gives rise to a situation where both importers and exporters want more oil, while almost all also face stagnating growth or even decrease in production. Again, this points to a 'supply-demand crunch' that is likely to have a major shaping impact on 21st-century societies. Indeed, a strong case can be made that just such a crunch is now in the process of unfolding in the form of increased competition and increased production costs due to declining EROI. To this we can add the prospect of historically unprecedented prices as the oil crunch takes hold, with further destabilising potential even as it improves the balance sheets of net exporters.

8. **Failed states and geopolitical disruptions.** Putting geological issues to one side for the moment, the geopolitics of oil must also be considered. After all, the first two major oil crises of the 20th century were geopolitical in nature, not geological, and yet the implications are remarkably similar: the consequence is a spike in oil prices. Of course, whether high prices result from geological or geopolitical supply constraints is of little relevance to oil-dependent economies. Either way, expensive oil tends to have disruptive, recessionary effects.

The importance of the geopolitical lens lies in the fact that a large proportion of global oil reserves is in politically unstable areas of the world, such as Iraq, Libya, Nigeria and Venezuela, or shipped through Egypt's Suez Canal. Oil supply chains can be highly vulnerable to social and political disruption, and this can have a strong impact on market dynamics. The US, for example, imports millions of barrels of oil each day from politically unstable nations, and Europe gets 80% of its oil from such regions.[61] The prospect of deepening instability in the Middle East or other major oil exporting regions is hardly unlikely or unforeseeable. Since this would likely cause significant disruption to global markets, oil-dependent societies may regret not being better prepared for the restricted supply and much higher prices such geopolitical disruption would bring.

The currently depressed oil price also plays havoc with the national incomes of many nations, which can itself lead to political instability.[62] An IMF study concludes that oil-exporting nations such as Russia, Iran and Venezuela need an oil price above $100 to balance their budgets.[63] The Saudi Arabian economy contracted for two straight quarters leading up to the end of 2017.[64] It is clear then that economic and geological issues quickly get intertwined with geopolitics, with potentially destabilising effects.

9. **Climate response.** In the next chapter we examine the climate question in some detail, but presently we simply note that peak oil and climate change cannot be considered separate or unrelated issues. It will not be much good if the world resolves the peak oil problem only to induce runaway climate change. Yet this trade-off is what seems to be happening. Tight oil (such as shale oil in the US) and the tar sands of Canada and Venezuela tend to be far more carbon-intensive than conventional oil.[65] But meeting growing oil demand means that those resources need to be produced and *are* being produced—the climate be damned.

If the world ever took climate change seriously, tar sands and shale oil would be the first oil resources to go, but as we've seen, they are the very resources that are propping up global production growth. A recent study suggests that growth in unconventional oil production is inconsistent with keeping global temperature from rising 2°C above pre-industrial levels, and that overall 35% of known oil reserves need to stay in the ground.[66] This suggests that even if there were no geological constraints on oil production, we should in effect be embracing peak oil now *by choice* and learning to live with a sharply declining oil supply, in order to have any chance of maintaining a safe climate system.

If a strong carbon tax incentivises that decline in oil demand, or if the divestment movement manages to undermine the financial support for fossil fuel production, then the problem of expensive oil again returns but through a different door. In oil-dependent societies, learning how to manage expensive oil should be a high priority, whether the high price is driven by geology, geopolitics, climate change mitigation or all those factors. Looking at the present situation from a different angle, the currently depressed price makes renewable energy alternatives less cost competitive. This works against the necessary transition beyond fossil fuels at a critical time, with disastrous implications for climate change mitigation. This ecological issue is typically overlooked by those analysts blinded by the apparent short-term economic benefits to consumers of cheaper oil. Herein lies the paradox of oil: the cheaper it is (economically), the more it costs (environmentally).[67]

10. **Fair distribution.** If the environment barely gets a mention in most peak oil analyses, social justice gets even less attention. Nevertheless, fair distribution of fossil fuels is one of the most powerful reasons oil-dependent societies *should*, we argue, be voluntarily embracing a world with less oil. The implications are complex but the logic is relatively straightforward. If the supply of oil in the ground is finite, then we need to ask how that oil should be used, for what purposes, and for whose benefit. If

climate change means that oil availability is (or should be) scarcer still, then distributive questions become even more pressing and important.

Global population is currently 7.6 billion. It is trending toward 9.8 billion by mid-century. If there is to be a fair distribution of available oil resources, the fact of resource finitude means that the rich world's energy-intensive societies need to significantly decrease their oil consumption. On a per capita basis, an average US citizen uses 22 barrels of oil per year, but the global average is only 4.6 barrels. In a world of 9.8 billion, an equal share of existing production would be only 3.5 barrels per year. Geophysical supply constraints mean only a fraction of that is assured in 2050. And even less, if oil is left in the ground in response to climate change. So even if all geological or geopolitical reasons for energy descent are dismissed, an ethical injunction remains: embrace energy descent not because we will have to (although soon enough we will), but in order to build a fairer world.

The dynamics of peak oil can be summarised as follows: as oil production slows or stagnates while demand continues to grow, oil prices increase until they retard or even reverse expected growth trajectories. Stagnating economies reduce their oil demand, leading to a crash in prices; low oil prices then facilitate economic recovery. With recovery comes increasing demand pressure, leading oil prices to rise till economic breaking point, and so on. As David Murphy and Charles Hall put it: 'increasing the oil supply to support economic growth will require high oil prices that will undermine that economic growth.'[68] We have also seen that low oil prices generally lead to reduced oil investment by oil companies, adding further complexities to market dynamics. This cycle of bust-recovery-bust is a recurring motif we may face in coming years and decades. It is ultimately economic stagnation or even contraction that we may have to prepare for. The world is unlikely to escape this unhappy cycle until it transitions beyond growth-dependent economies and breaks its addiction to oil.

This point about breaking our addiction to oil deserves some brief elaboration here, because it raises the spectre of what physicist Tom Murphy has called the 'energy trap'.[69] In order to break the addiction, economies dependent on oil will need to invest huge amounts of engineering effort, money and energy, plus myriad other resources, in building new social and economic infrastructures. This includes such measures as efficient public transport systems to incentivise people to drive less, organic food systems, renewable energy systems, and highly localised production and supply chains. The building effort will itself be subject to significant dependence on the oil it seeks to displace.

But since this transition has barely begun, the necessary investment may well be required at a time when money and energy are scarcer than they have been in recent decades. This places us in an 'energy trap' of the following form: politicians are going to have a short-term incentive *not* to invest extra money and energy in new infrastructure, since in coming years people will increasingly be feeling the pinch of higher oil price and its related economic impacts. This means that the surplus money and energy for the necessary infrastructure projects will be increasingly difficult to come by. Kicking the can down the road will provide some short-term relief for people and politicians. But while this will be seductive as a political strategy, it cannot remove the inevitable need for that new, post-petroleum infrastructure. In fact any delay only exacerbates the problem—the inevitable investment will come at a time when energy and money are scarcer still, when oil itself is probably even more costly, and the time frame for change is tighter.

* * * * *

Peak oil is proving to be a more complex phenomenon than theorists originally anticipated. It is not playing out as a precise 'moment' or 'event', but rather as a dynamic interaction between various forces that have provoked some adaptive adjustments (such as demand destruction and increased investment in shale) that in turn influence the situation in multidimensional ways. There may never be a 'shock moment' to signal peak oil's arrival; instead, we may continue to experience peak oil as a gradual, unplanned, and largely misunderstood transition to new patterns of energy use and economic production that are less oil dependent, giving rise to social, economic and ecological impacts that no one can predict with any certainty.

The evolving interrelationship of geological, geopolitical, economic, cultural and technological variables has continued to surprise analysts—from the 'cornucopians', who claim there is nothing to worry about, to the 'doomsayers', who think global socio-economic collapse is imminent, and everyone in between. No doubt there are twists still to come in this energy tale. But it seems clear that the consequences of peak oil are not going away.

Whether the next twist arrives in the form of a new war or financial crisis, a new technology suite, a bursting shale bubble, or perhaps a radical cultural shift away from fossil fuels in response to climatic instability, intellectual integrity demands that analysts continue to revise viewpoints as further evidence comes to light. This issue is too important to be governed by ideology.

The point of this chapter has been to highlight a geological reality in economic context: oil is finite and subject to depletion, even as oil demand seems set to continue its historic growth. This is a potential recipe for disaster, unless our energy intensive societies act quickly to wean themselves off fossil fuels and build societal resilience in preparation for ongoing fossil energy depletion. And looking beyond oil, a recent study finds that all fossil fuel production (oil, gas and coal) may peak around 2025.[70] While a coal peak may be driven by reduced demand, any peak in gas or oil is likely to be driven fundamentally by geological depletion, since demand is expected to increase. In the age of Twitter, the year 2025 may seem like a long way off, but in terms of an energy transition as fundamental as this, the challenge is essentially upon us already, if only more of us knew it.

As noted briefly earlier, there is some scope for substitution between oil, gas and coal. As such, the range of responses by various actors to respective peaks in production of each energy source will inevitably be broader than we have covered here. It's worth considering that the actions taken will not necessarily be aligned with the best outcomes from an environmental point of view, or socially in terms of fair distribution, when considered collectively at the global scale. From a climate perspective especially, the substitution of coal-derived fuels for oil, in order to delay the eventual need to rethink transport and supply chains, could have particularly severe consequences. It also makes anticipating the timing of fossil energy peaks and their consequences a fraught endeavour.

Nonetheless, while fossil energy depletion might seem slow to us now, from a macro-historical perspective it will not be long before the brevity of carbon civilisation becomes apparent. The fossil fuel windfall through which humanity is burning in a few centuries took on the rough order of half a billion years to accumulate. We're using them *a million times faster* than they formed. We can expect posterity to reflect on the shocking and bewildering speed with which humanity spent—and in so many ways wasted—its one-off inheritance of energy-rich coal, gas and oil. Our carbon civilisation is but a brief anomaly in geological time, a blink of the eye, whose existence is already in the process of decay. It is like a castle built from sand, soon to be washed away by a rising tide, never to return. One way or another, this century will be the one in which carbon civilisation disappears, although its environmental and material legacy will doubtless live on, for centuries and beyond. It turns out we lacked the maturity and wisdom to wield such awesome energetic power and wealth, sadly resembling the child who won the lottery and spent the entire proceeds immediately on candy and toys, only to be left sick and dissatisfied. For many of those attuned to the situation unfolding, the knot of regret is beginning to tighten in our collective gut, threatening to evolve into despair.

It will now be shown, however, that humanity's challenges run much deeper than peak oil and the depletion of fossil energy. Arguably the more pressing problem, it turns out, is not how little fossil energy we have available—but how much.

Chapter 4. Climate Change, Carbon Budgets and the Economics of Deep Decarbonisation

Geological timescales often span tens of thousands or even tens of millions of years or more. Today, however, we live in what is increasingly referred to by scientists as 'the Anthropocene', the first epoch in which collective human actions can be viewed as constituting forces of geological significance. The Anthropocene is barely three hundred years old, a consequence of industrialisation and the carbon civilisation enabled by fossil fuels. No environmental disturbance more clearly represents the Anthropocene than climate change. Human activity on the planet is now so imposing that we are destabilising something as fundamental as the climate system. The future viability of conditions necessary to support much current life on earth, humans included, is being threatened by impacts such as ongoing global warming, sea level rise, and the increased regularity and severity of extreme weather events (including droughts, floods and storms).

If we do not respond swiftly and appropriately to this existential threat, it seems our story may not so much resemble the frog that did not know it was being slowly boiled, as the human killed when the hair dryer fell (or was it pulled?) into the bath. The tragic imagery is figurative and polemical, but unfortunately the scientific account of the origins of this crisis is robust. In the human story's cosmological context, this environmental disruption is occurring strikingly fast, yet its consequences will be felt for millennia.

Modelling of the relationship between greenhouse gas (GHG) emissions and associated temperature rise is a central focus for climate research. Climate scientists draw on various methodologies to model the climate system's response to emissions, in order to estimate the temperature increase that will result from a given emission profile. The relationship between temperature and emissions reflects the model builders' understanding of how the actual physical system being modelled behaves, often as it interacts with other Earth systems. In this respect, climate modelling is similar in nature to any conceptual modelling effort aimed at understanding the future behaviour of large-scale, complex phenomena. Findings from such analyses differ depending on modelling methodology, on the way that a particular methodology is implemented, and on the input parameter values for a particular model run. By looking at the findings across a large set of runs, often from multiple models, scientists arrive at an estimate of the probability distribution for temperature increase with a given level of cumulative emissions over a given time period. This is the foundation of what is called 'carbon budget analysis', a term that has entered the lexicon of climate scientists over the last decade. Defined further below, a carbon budget essentially refers to the maximum amount of GHG emissions that can be released into the atmosphere if the goal is to prevent global temperatures from rising a specified level above the pre-industrial baseline.

The size and shape of a carbon budget is dependent on a range of parameters, each of which will contribute to increasing or decreasing the emissions limit, thus making this easier or more challenging to remain within. Key parameters include: What temperature rise above pre-industrial levels are we trying to avoid? What probability of success or failure is considered justified? What is the understanding of the relationship between anthropogenic GHG emissions and global temperature underpinning the modelling methodology that informs the budget? What assumptions are being made about the role of carbon-capture-and-storage (CCS) and negative emissions technologies (NETs)? And beyond the question of a carbon budget's overall magnitude, there is the question of how it should be distributed between and within nations. The choice of different values for these parameters has inevitable socio-economic implications, and this draws the scientific analyses into more normative, value-laden or 'politicised' spaces.

This is a very active area of research at present. Significant new findings have come to light during the course of writing this book, and these have in fact increased the range of emission budget estimates for remaining below a given global temperature threshold. With respect to the Paris Agreement's aspiration to limit temperature increase to 1.5°C this century, some investigators find that the budget for a 66% probability of achieving this is higher than indicated by previous research, while others find that it is now lower.[71] Depending on the methodology employed, the budgets reported in recently published studies range from -192 Gt CO_2 (i.e. the budget is already exceeded by this amount) to 693 Gt CO_2 (approximately 15 years emissions at current global rate).[72]

Despite the inherent uncertainty to which this points, the science underpinning carbon budget analysis is generally regarded as sufficiently robust to inform sound policy making. Considered collectively, the overall message is that the world is now at a point where emissions must be reduced to zero as quickly as possible for any realistic possibility of meeting the Paris Agreement's aspirational target.[73] Nonetheless, most scientists, politicians, economists and the broader public have been slow to recognise the radical socio-economic and political implications of carbon budget analysis. Below we summarise the key issues in relation to the state of the science at the time of writing, discuss some normative questions, and draw out the most significant and challenging implications. Ultimately, we conclude, for reasons to be explained, that in the carbon-intensive societies of the rich world, responding adequately to the climate crisis means accepting the inevitability of energy descent and seeking viable futures within the conditions this implies rather than fighting against them.

4.1 Temperature threshold

To begin with, where should the temperature threshold be set? This is one of the most important questions to answer when framing a carbon budget, and yet there is no objective way to decide the matter. The underlying logic, however, is clear: the lower the threshold, the safer the climate for existing human and natural systems, but the smaller the carbon budget—and vice versa. In recent decades a maximum 2 °C temperature rise above pre-industrial levels has commonly been assumed to represent a 'safe' threshold, beyond which humanity would enter increasingly 'dangerous' territory. However, there is growing recognition among scientists that a temperature rise of 2 °C is far too risky. This emerging consensus came to inform the Paris Agreement of 2015, in which almost all nations of the world committed to keeping temperatures 'well below' 2 °C and, as mentioned earlier, 'to pursue efforts to limit the temperature increase … to 1.5 °C.'[74] It is worth noting that the proposed allowable temperature rise is a global average surface temperature. We can expect this average to be associated with significant geographical variation in temperature change. Further, it will be the highly populated, least well-off regions that are likely to suffer the greatest impacts.

Given the climate impacts the world is already experiencing at 1 °C, we contend that 1.5 °C should really be considered a maximum threshold, not an aspiration to pursue. Indeed, at 1.5 °C above pre-industrial levels, the science indicates that many low-lying islands and coastal cities are at grave risk of being submerged; the Great Barrier Reef will likely be degraded over much of its extent[75] ; food security will be seriously threatened for significant portions of the global population; and melting permafrosts may well release enough methane to trigger further temperature rise even if anthropogenic emissions have ceased.[76] It's for such reasons that the 1.5 °C threshold was included in the Paris Agreement as an aspiration. But it is difficult to see how, if this aspiration is not met, settling for a maximum threshold beyond 1.5 °C could possibly be consistent with the IPCC's adoption of the precautionary principle. Climate stability is not something with which we should be gambling.

4.2 Probability of success

The second key normative question concerns what probability of success is considered appropriate. Given the complexities and interrelationships between Earth systems, climate scientists discuss their climate change scenarios in terms of probabilities, not certainties. For example, if a particular temperature threshold goal is assumed (e.g. 1.5°C or 2°C), scientists can advise on how much carbon can be emitted for a given probability (e.g. 50%, 66%, 80% or 95% chance) of not exceeding that threshold. And in addition to the uncertainty associated with how temperature will increase with increasing GHG emissions, there is uncertainty with respect to changes to, for example, weather and sea level rise that will accompany a given temperature rise. This raises normative questions about what probability of meeting climate targets can be considered as justified. The higher the probability of successfully meeting those goals, the lower the carbon budget. Conversely, the greater the readiness to risk exceeding a given temperature threshold, the more carbon can be emitted.

Scientists believe that exceeding a 2°C temperature rise is likely to be extremely dangerous,[77] so it would seem that a very high probability of successfully avoiding that outcome is warranted. That is why the international community has now stated 1.5°C should be deemed the maximum temperature threshold. When the consequences of a given outcome are relatively innocuous, a course of action with a greater chance of failing to avoid that outcome can be tolerated. But when the consequences have potential to be extremely dangerous, even catastrophic, then it is only reasonable to take substantial precautions and expect a high probability of success when acting to avoid such an outcome. After all, would you cross the road if you had a 50% or 66% chance of doing so safely? Would you do so if you had an 80% chance? A 95% chance? Probably not, and yet it seems the world is basing climate policy on far lower expectations of success. The IEA tends to use 50% chance of avoiding 2°C; the IPCC develops 1.5°C and 2°C scenarios on 50% and 66% chances of success, but no higher. This normalises a one-in-two or one-in-three chance of failure.

Why such low probability expectations of success? Sadly, the answer is political and economic, not scientific or moral. For instance, if world leaders concluded on reviewing the evidence that an 80% chance of remaining below 1.5°C was the most justifiable climate goal, they would then discover that there is in fact no carbon budget left,[78] just as there is no carbon budget if a 90% chance of avoiding 2 °C is assumed.[79] Public acknowledgement of this would constitute a form of global emergency declaration, signalling the need for radical transformation of societies to manage the swiftest decarbonisation possible. But rather than accept this implication, mainstream political and economic analyses essentially 'self-censor' their own work in order to avoid questioning the dominant economic paradigm of growth-oriented market capitalism.[80]

It is also worth noting that there are some worrying ambiguities in the very language of a '1.5 °C scenario'. When such a scenario is presented as having a 50% chance of success, typically overlooked is that this actually means a 33% chance of exceeding 2 °C and a 10% chance of exceeding 3 °C.[81] A study by two US security think tanks concluded that 3 °C of warming and 0.5 m of sea level rise would likely lead to 'outright chaos'.[82] If there is 10% chance of exceeding 3 °C and causing outright chaos, how defensible is it to call this a '1.5 °C scenario'?

Several of these so-called 1.5 °C carbon budget scenarios based on low chances of success (e.g. 50% or 66%) have been published. Even these relatively unambitious scenarios show that based on current emissions of around 40 Gt/year, such a budget will be blown in about four years. Some leading scientists consider this an over-estimate.[83] Given that emissions are still increasing—in 2017 they increased 2% over 2016—four years seems like a maximum time frame; and again, aiming for a higher probability of success means there is no carbon budget left. This has led some commentators to talk with good reason of the 'myth of "burnable carbon"'.[84]

4.3 Carbon-capture-and-storage and negative emissions technologies

A third normative question concerns the assumptions that should be made about the role of carbon-capture-and-storage (CCS) and negative emissions technologies (NETs) in mitigating climate change. CCS involves capturing the carbon dioxide (CO_2) produced in coal- or gas-fired power stations and burying it underground. NETs include practices like planting up large areas of land with carbon-sequestering trees and plants; seaweed and algal farming; biochar production; and ocean fertilisation. CCS and NETs can even be combined in an approach called 'biomass energy carbon capture and storage' (BECCS), which involves planting carbon-sequestering trees and eventually burning the wood to produce electricity while capturing and storing the combustion emissions.

The more carbon that is captured or sequestered, the more fossil fuels we can burn—and again, vice versa. The normative implication of proposals to deploy CCS at large scale derives from the fact that it is not currently commercially viable. For NETs, this follows from various impediments such as being technically unproven, expensive, slow to implement, not currently deployable at the scale needed, or presenting adverse consequences for competing land uses, such as food production and biodiversity.[85] As such, bold assumptions must be made about the future viability and even desirability of these strategies. Whether or not such assumptions are valid is inherently uncertain. In many cases, validity will only be established through the social learning that comes with serious attempts at large-scale deployment. Put otherwise, we must make value-laden judgements about how much we are prepared to gamble on mitigation strategies for which the probability of success is unknown—and often even unknowable.

It seems we are gambling wildly. Of the 116 2°C scenarios included in the IPCC Fifth Assessment Report (AR5), 101 of them involve sucking vast amounts of carbon out of the atmosphere, chiefly via BECCS.[86] It is estimated that 'negative emissions' of this scale would require land between one and three times the size of India,[87] and as much water as is currently used for global agriculture.[88] At present no national climate policy mentions BECCS.[89] There is currently one working project in the world, a relatively small, repurposed corn ethanol plant in Decatur, Illinois. Worryingly, it seems that international political discourse on climate has come to rely on a technology that is theoretically plausible but at present is for all practical purposes non-existent.

Climate scientists Kevin Anderson (based at the Tyndall Centre for Climate Research) and Glen Peters (based at the Centre for International Climate and Energy Policy) call CCS and NETs an 'unjust and high-stakes gamble' and 'a moral hazard'.[90] Resting on the dubious assumption that vast amounts of carbon can be captured and sequestered in the future, these mitigation strategies reduce the pressure to wind back fossil fuel use today, and so are simply the latest justification for delaying decarbonisation of economies.

Efforts to quantify future potential for carbon dioxide absorption by forests and emission reduction by CCS are subject to irreducible uncertainty and hence must be regarded as speculative. They may be politically attractive, but reliance on them cannot claim scientific legitimacy. What if it turns out CCS never becomes viable at a sufficiently significant scale? In 2017 one of the few CCS pilot projects shut down as budget estimates blew out.[91] What if land, food or water pressures, or forest fires, mean assumed carbon planting never eventuates or never succeeds at the scale necessary? These are very real possibilities, but if we act today as if CCS and NETs will be successful and they end up failing, then the carbon budget for a safe climate will be blown, perhaps catastrophically. This would then necessitate even more challenging (and perhaps unrealisable) decarbonisation strategies.

Anderson and others make a compelling case that it would be better not to assume CCS and NETs will scale up significantly, and act on that basis. If it turns out some such technologies can scale up, then all the better. Mainstream analyses, however, do not proceed on that basis because it would shrink the available carbon budget so drastically that mitigation strategies would clearly be incompatible with continued economic growth, on which all modern economies presently rely. Essentially all mainstream pathways for atmospheric carbon mitigation, including those based on the IPCC assessments, make extremely bold assumptions about CCS and NETs in the tortured hope that world economies can grow themselves out of the climate problem. That the economics of growth might be causing this problem is unthinkable—or, at least, unspeakable.

In addition to CCS and NETs, there is the prospect of geoengineering. Given the enormous effort needed to draw carbon dioxide back down from the atmosphere or to capture it before it is discharged in the first place, geoengineering could well be seen as a simpler and faster alternative to limit surface temperature increase. It could be particularly attractive as its benefits may be local (though they also may not be), and it would not require international agreement. Of course, geoengineering fails to solve any of the other problems associated with humanity's dependence on fossil fuels, and there is also the very real prospect of geoengineering causing new forms of climatic instability if (when!) such unprecedented experiments take unexpected turns.[92]

4.4 Distributive considerations

For present purposes, the final normative question to outline—and one of the most important and complex—concerns distributive issues. *This* question can only be asked once a global carbon budget has been derived.[93] Having answered the previous questions, we are then faced with the further question of how the resultant global carbon budget should be distributed between and within nations. Should it be assumed that every person gets an equal share of the remaining carbon budget? Should those most responsible for historical emissions get a smaller share? What should be done if there is little or no carbon budget left?

Our own basic intuitions of distributive fairness suggest to us that those who have contributed most (and benefited most) from historic carbon emissions should have a smaller share of any remaining carbon budget. Imagine you are at a party where a pizza has been served, but someone ate six of the eight slices before most of the guests arrived. Should we now share the two remaining slices equally amongst everyone present? Or should the person who ate the first six slices get less or none?

While we acknowledge that arriving at an uncontroversial basis for distributing any carbon budget is likely to be impossible in our postmodern age, a powerful case can be made that those who have benefited the most from fossil fuel consumption historically do not have grounds to expect an equal share of any remaining budget. If only very limited quantities of fossil fuel can still be burnt, surely it is more morally reasonable and ethically defensible to invest the vast majority of any carbon budget in lifting the poorest out of poverty? Few would be so bold as to suggest this approach is a likely outcome. But any person who claims to seek a fair world should at least be prepared to acknowledge what such an outcome would entail. This distributive perspective provides yet further support for seeking viable futures within the context of energy descent—again, not because we have to (although we do) but because we should.

4.5 The economics of deep decarbonisation

We conclude our examination of carbon budgets by briefly unpacking the economics of deep decarbonisation. Doing so shines a light on the radical and often unappreciated implications of even the most lenient carbon budget analyses. Here we deliberately make assumptions favourable to rich nations. The purpose of doing so is simply to show that, even then, the required decarbonisation rates cannot be achieved merely through efficiency gains but must involve significant reduction in demand for underlying energy services. The tight coupling between economic activity as currently practised and availability of energy services implies that the extent of the reduction would be incompatible with continued economic growth.

Suppose, for example, that the world settled on a carbon budget that was framed by a relatively unambitious mitigation goal, based on a 50% chance of keeping temperature rise under 2°C. Suppose further that the models assume that emissions in the poorer nations somehow manage to peak in 2025 and decline thereafter at an unprecedented rate of 7% per year. Based on these assumptions—which are extremely favourable to rich world economies—Kevin Anderson and Alice Bows have shown that in order to keep within the available carbon budget the rich nations would need to decarbonise at 8–10% per year. Note that those figures were published in 2011, and since then the world has been emitting about 36 Gt of carbon dioxide each year, meaning that today the required decarbonisation rates would be steeper still.

Even mainstream climate economists such as Nicholas Stern argue that economic growth as measured by GDP is incompatible with decarbonisation rates over 3–4% per year.[94] Efficiency alone cannot be expected to achieve decarbonisation above that rate, and renewables or nuclear cannot be scaled up fast enough. As a consequence, emission reductions this steep must be supplemented by significantly reduced demand for energy services dependent on fossil fuels. Figure 4 shows the relationship between world GDP and carbon dioxide emissions from fossil fuels. Add this view to the story told in Figure 1 (world GDP versus total primary energy use), and the implied economic trajectory becomes clear. The close connection between energy use and economic growth means that significantly reduced energy services will result in less physical production and consumption. That is precisely the conclusion mainstream analysts are desperate to avoid. But that is the implication of even conservative carbon budget analyses. Indeed, Kevin Anderson even argues that planned economic contraction, or 'degrowth', is necessary if the rich nations are to avoid a carbon budget blowout.[95]

Here is the most challenging aspect of these calculations. The above carbon budget analysis—based on merely a 50% chance of avoiding a 2°C temperature rise—is no longer in line even with mainstream political and economic rhetoric. If, for example, we aimed for a 50% chance of avoiding a 1.5°C rise, or a 66% or 80% chance of avoiding a 1.5°C, then obviously the decarbonisation rates outlined would not be 8–10% per year but far higher, making continued economic growth even less compatible with a safe climate. Consequently, if the world is serious about keeping within a carbon budget for a safe climate, the rich nations must not only vastly increase the carbon efficiency of each unit of economic output, but must use far less energy and materials. Given the centrality of energy and materials to economic growth, it seems the only coherent response to the climate crisis is for rich nations to embrace a degrowth strategy of planned economic contraction.[96] We acknowledge the realpolitik implausibility of a strategy so framed receiving mainstream embrace, and return to this matter in Chapter 6. But leaving aside for the moment the typically messy pragmatics of human political relations,

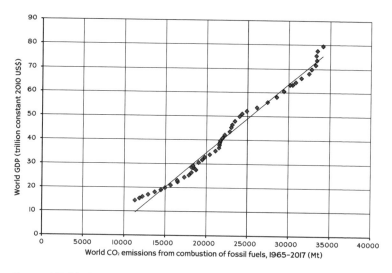

Figure 4: World GDP versus total carbon dioxide emissions for consumption of coal, oil and gas, for the period 1965–2017. The strong correlation between GDP and CO_2 emissions from fossil fuel combustion is apparent, with $R^2 = 0.9843$ for the linear trend line shown ($y = 0.0029x - 22.63$). Note the sudden onset of an apparent decoupling trend for the three data points immediately prior to the last point. This is associated with very low growth in CO_2 emissions in these years, with trend GDP growth. Most recent data (the right-most data point in the figure) indicates discontinuity in this trend in 2017, with CO_2 emissions resuming faster growth. The 2017 data point shown is based on estimated CO_2 emissions growth of 2% (Global Carbon Project) and GDP growth of 3% (World Bank). Data sources: world GDP, World Bank; CO_2 emissions from fossil fuels, BP Statistical Review of World Energy.

the case for degrowth set out here simply follows in our view from a sober assessment of the evidence. Whether this conclusion is palatable is a different question.

In the context of this book, the key point can be summarised as follows: even relatively unambitious carbon budget analyses require decarbonisation rates that cannot be achieved merely through efficiency gains. Nor can those decarbonisation rates be achieved by a wholesale shift to renewable or nuclear energy sources, given the time needed for such sources to scale up. Therefore, to achieve the decarbonisation rates required for a safe climate, the rich world (our focus here) needs to use far less energy, which implies reduced availability of energy *services*, which in turn implies degrowth. Achieving a safe climate therefore means accepting the inevitability of energy descent, and working within such conditions even before energy descent is imposed upon us from fossil energy depletion.

Chapter 5. Nuclear and Renewables: The Potential and Limitations of Alternative Energy Sources

When the extraordinary but finite nature of fossil energy is appreciated, the fact of its ongoing depletion and imminent decline offers reason enough to prepare for an era defined in terms very different to the energy abundance and energy affordability that, particularly in rich nations, is enjoyed today. When the steep decarbonisation rates for a safe climate are appreciated, as dictated by even relatively unambitious carbon budget analyses, planning and preparing for an era of energy descent, rather than energy growth and abundance, emerges as an unavoidable necessity. And yet such planning and preparation remains on the fringe of energy discourse. Why?

The main reason for this myopia, we contend, is that mainstream analyses and media have been captured, consciously or unconsciously, by a seductive but flawed vision of 'green growth' which itself is underpinned by a blinding techno-optimism. This ideology essentially holds that technology and market mechanisms will be able to decarbonise and dematerialise affluent living standards sufficiently to allow those living standards to be globalised in a sustainable way. Thus, the argument goes, a globally growing economy can be maintained into some indefinite future, without undermining environmental and ecological conditions conducive to human flourishing. On this view, the high levels of energy and resource use in rich nations do not need to be questioned; instead, what needs to happen is for the high impact modes of production to become more efficient.

This growth reliance has been under sustained critique in recent decades.[97] Nevertheless, it remains the dominant political and economic ideology governing the world today. While much more could be said about this broad, complex and ongoing controversy, this chapter aims to examine the 'green growth' vision specifically through the lens of energy. Underlying the green growth paradigm is the assumption that we do not need to embrace a future of significantly reduced energy *demand*, we simply need to 'green' or 'decarbonise' the *supply* of energy, whether that is via renewable energy sources, like wind, solar and biofuels, or via nuclear energy sources. It is widely believed that such sources and their associated conversion technologies will avoid the climate problem and resolve peak oil concerns before they disrupt the status quo too significantly.

We are wholly in favour of transcending fossil fuels and initiating a swift decarbonisation of the global economy. Nevertheless, we will offer a sobering assessment of the potential for various alternative energy sources to replace the vast energy foundations of carbon civilisation with 'green energy'. Yes, it is clear humanity must embrace alternative energy sources, due to both the inevitability of fossil energy depletion and climate change mitigation. But our review of the evidence and arguments suggests that those alternative sources are highly unlikely to maintain or grow the levels of energy services provided by existing fossil fuel-dominated global energy supply. More directly, we maintain that the limitations of those alternatives are such that, in the rich world at least, a post-carbon transition implies energy descent.

Unfortunately, this is an area of debate in which competing schools of thought—'renewable advocates' vs. 'nuclear advocates'—hold what often seem to be commitments of an almost religious nature to their particular energy solution. Too often the debate degenerates into destructive battles. It recently led to a renewable advocate, Mark Jacobson, initiating (but eventually dropping) legal proceedings against critics.[98] We approach the debate with more circumspection, knowing that the current situation is uncertain, meaning that future energy transitions are uncertain. But that very uncertainty ends up actually supporting the case for energy descent preparation and planning, in ways to be explained. While most of this analysis will focus on the limitations of renewable energy, we begin with a brief consideration of nuclear energy.

5.1 The potential and limitations of nuclear energy

The essentials of the case for nuclear are relatively straightforward, at least in the abstract. Advocates argue that nuclear generation provides a relatively low-carbon source of electricity; that the technology is available today and improving; and that the geopolitical, security and environmental safety concerns can be managed. Given the various limitations of renewable energy sources, such as their intermittency (discussed below), nuclear advocates also argue that in the absence of fossil fuels, the need to provide dispatchable power (i.e. power that can be delivered on-demand at a specific future time) at sufficient rates leaves no practical option available other than nuclear.[99] Given the favourable power densities that can be achieved with nuclear generation, this form of electricity supply also requires less land than solar or wind farms. Although the economics of nuclear are highly contested and complex, defenders contend that nuclear is the cheapest form of low-carbon electricity at the system level. Arguments such as these have even persuaded some of the world's most prominent climate activists, including scientist James Hansen and journalist George Monbiot, to defend nuclear energy. So what are the prospects for nuclear? And what are the challenges?

One way to think about whether nuclear energy could or should be the primary means of replacing fossil energy is to consider how many nuclear power plants would be needed to do this. Physicist Joshua Pearce points out that to meet the equivalent of global primary energy demand in 2004 via electricity, the world would have needed approximately 14,500 nuclear power plants of 1 GW capacity each.[100] And to meet anticipated primary energy demand in 2050 while cutting 2004 energy emissions by 60%, the world would need to build a total of 26,000 such plants. This is a rough rule-of-thumb only, as it doesn't account for the distinction between primary energy and final energy. Providing the latter entirely as electricity could result in an annual supply task that is in the order of 60% of the equivalent fossil fuel primary energy. On the other hand, Pearce's figures are based on a now out-of-date reduction target for 2004 GHG emissions of only 60%. If we take the figure of 26,000 nuclear plants of 1 GW capacity as broadly indicative, then to put this figure in context, currently the world has 449 nuclear power plants, with only 60 new ones (20 of them in China) under construction. Furthermore, significant numbers of existing nuclear plants are nearing the end of their design lives and are due for decommissioning in coming years.

The full implications of such a task can be debated to some extent. Technologies can and will advance; a major effort to increase the deployment rate could be expected to result in considerably reduced construction times and costs. But the general point remains: many thousands of nuclear power plants would need to be built to replace aggregate fossil energy supply (or even to replace a half or a quarter of this). Yet in much of the world there is intense social and political backlash whenever a single new nuclear power plant is proposed. Imagine planning for ten or twenty thousand new sites!

Since Fukushima, the prospect of a nuclear renaissance looks slim at best, with nuclear power stations actually producing less electricity today than ten years ago. Rightly or wrongly, people generally do not want to live in the vicinity of nuclear power plants and, even if a modest number of proposed sites get approved, which is to be expected, it seems highly unlikely that the social and political obstacles lying in the way of a vastly expanded nuclear industry will be swept aside. Advocates argue that this social and political resistance is misinformed, a result of environmentalist scare-mongering designed to advance the cause of renewables. But it cannot be denied that scaling up the nuclear industry to decarbonise the global economy (assuming it can be done) would increase the likelihood of nuclear accidents, increase the amount of nuclear waste that must be managed into the distant future, and increase the available targets for high-impact terrorist attacks.

As well as these barriers, expansion of currently commercial nuclear technology appears hamstrung by crippling capital costs, calling the economics into question at a time when the financial costs of renewables are unambiguously on the decline. Perhaps the greatest challenge to nuclear, however, is the seemingly impossible timeline it faces as a climate mitigation technology: given that it generally takes 10 years or more for regulatory approval and construction of a nuclear plant, rollout rates that would make a globally material difference on the climate front stretch the limits of plausibility. Generation IV 'intrinsically safe' reactors that greatly reduce waste concerns and massively expand the scope of current fuel reserves look good on paper, but significant R&D remains, with the most advanced effort at pilot stage only.[101] Practical fusion power continues to be at best a theoretical possibility many decades in the future, despite many billions of dollars of past and ongoing investment.[102]

A further challenge to nuclear (shared by the major renewable energy sources of wind and solar) is the fact that it produces electricity, when currently electricity is only about 18% of global final energy demand. So even if these alternative energy sources were able to satisfy total global electricity demand, this still leaves around 82% of non-electricity final energy demand that is currently carbon-based. Often overlooked, the hardest part of any post-carbon transition is figuring out how to deal with the liquid fuels problem, since oil powers over 90% of global transport and, along with coal and gas, a variety of energy-intense industrial processes that, at this stage at least, cannot be powered by electricity on a sufficiently large scale. Of course, the theoretical answer to this problem is to figure out how to electrify the entire global economy. But with industrial infrastructures having been shaped by fossil energy for two centuries, and with oil driving the global integration of supply chains, the challenge of moving away from incumbent energy carriers can hardly be overstated. We will discuss the electrification issue further in our detailed examination of renewables.

On balance, it is our non-dogmatic view that nuclear energy is going to play a continuing role in global energy systems for many decades ahead. But we also see its role as most likely being limited to a minor fraction of total final energy use, probably continuing its relatively flat levels of electricity production, perhaps increasing in significance, but perhaps even declining in coming years as old plants are decommissioned faster than new plants are brought on-line. Given that any serious climate response means decarbonising the global economy over the next few decades (at most), and given how long it takes to bring a single nuclear plant on-line, the pressing deployment timeline seems too tight for such technology to be relied on much more heavily.

This points towards futures in which powering human societies primarily—and as close as possible to 'entirely'—with renewable sources appears to be our present best bet. In overall energy terms, it looks like wind turbines and solar PV arrays will need to do most of the heavy lifting. Questions of whether it's *feasible* to power human societies in this way then naturally come to the fore.

5.2 Can the global economy run entirely on renewables?

There's a rich irony here: it's of course *absolutely* established that 100% renewably powered societies are feasible, by the simple fact of viable non-industrial human ways of life over the vast majority of our species' existence. A great diversity of distinct human social forms demonstrates the adequacy of synchronous earth energy flows for successful functioning. But renewable energy (RE) feasibility research overwhelmingly has a narrower focus. In essence, it asks whether currently commercial and close-to-market RE conversion technologies can support industrial, growth-oriented societies and economies functionally equivalent to those in place today.

In response to this research question we hear a lot about the polarised perspectives holding that current renewable technologies *absolutely can* or *absolutely cannot* provide the scope and scale of energy services currently provided by fossil fuels. The extent to which RE technologies can replace or, as many envisage, even expand beyond carbon civilisation's fossil energy foundations is too often answered by ideology, rather than by comprehensive economic, engineering and scientific inquiry. We humans have a strong tendency to believe what we want to believe. For instance, environmentalists who are deeply concerned about climate change, energy depletion and the possible impacts of nuclear disasters have inherent motivation to support renewable energy. But often it seems that this *desire* for renewable alternatives to fossil fuels and nuclear fission translates into a *faith* in the feasibility and affordability of such alternatives.

There's a broad middle-ground though that tends to have a lower public profile. These are the many serious and highly-informed investigators who support the transition to renewable energy to whatever extent is possible, and who at the same time regard the nature of future energy systems—and, often, the forms of economy and society that they enable—to be uncertain.

Many in this middle-ground share a commitment to thinking critically about the roles and prospects for RE conversion technologies. Thinking critically is not the same as being a 'renewable energy critic' or 'anti-renewable energy'. It involves carefully considering the contexts for knowledge claims, including the confidence with which one can regard knowledge generated in a particular context as holding for others. This seems to be important for developing an appreciation for the nature and status of human knowledge that can support collaborative learning and action. We ask that the following critical inquiry into the potential and limitations of RE be received in that spirit—as seeking to deepen the understanding of an area that is presently, and will remain for some time at the very least, subject to major uncertainties.

5.3 Making sense of model-based feasibility assessments: a map is not the territory

When findings from any conceptual modelling exercise are claimed to prove the feasibility (or non-feasibility) of transition to 100% RE, careful critical interpretation is always called for. Many such studies have been conducted to date and, when they are published by government organisations or in prestigious scientific journals, people are inclined to assume the conclusions can be accepted at face value. Media outlets often review the headline findings of these studies, typically superficially and without critical insight. Indeed, given the complexity of the issues under consideration, it can require considerable expertise to understand such studies (which are often long, technical and dull). In a busy world people may be inclined to assume that the peer-review process provides sufficient assurance of authority and that the latest modelling exercise demonstrates a transition to 100% RE faces no technical, economic or practical barriers—and, moreover, that the engineering challenges confronting such an undertaking are all in hand.

But models do not *prove* what can be achieved in the real world. Modelling outcomes are a function of the assumptions on which models are constructed. As such, any proof is relative to a model's limited context, and not the actual situation within which the envisaged change process would need to be realised in practice. What is assumed to be relevant for a particular model is a function of the modeller's worldview, and worldviews give rise to perspectives that are unavoidably partial. The real world always holds surprises in store, and it is very difficult to 'out-smart' it when grappling with a situation of the size and complexity entailed by rapid global transformation of humanity's tightly coupled economy-energy systems.

If a key feasibility study assumption turns out to be flawed, the entire conclusion can be called into question. If many or all of the assumptions are dubious, then the uncertainty or implausibility of the conclusion compounds. When serious critics examine high-profile models that claim to prove feasibility for transition to 100% renewable energy over territories ranging from regional to global scale, they typically find that these exercises are informed by many uncertainties and contestable assumptions. It follows that 'real world' inferences extrapolated from such research should be viewed as speculative at best.[103]

Exercises of this nature certainly play an important role in the scoping process for any large-scale engineering initiative. But transition of energy systems globally away from fossil fuels represents an engineering undertaking of utterly unprecedented and breathtaking scale. Conceptual modelling is only the very first rudimentary step in figuring out what might be possible in practice, and what efforts might be involved in realising such a vision. Its utility is in the way that it interacts with and informs the design, construction, operational management and maintenance activities of engineers, experience that can then feed back to improve subsequent modelling efforts, in a process of continuous action learning. The actual engineering practice of building plant and infrastructure, and then operating it over extended periods, is absolutely essential to this learning, however. It is in the strictest sense 'learning by doing'. *Knowing* and *doing* are inseparable here: certainty can only be claimed with respect to what has been done and shown to be effective in practice. Even then, the applicability of knowledge developed in one context to another demands that a great deal of care be taken in understanding the equivalence of those contexts.

The central message here is that the status of claims based on conceptual modelling exercises alone—that is, where these relate to initiatives that have never before been attempted and for which there is no equivalent precedent—are best treated with a healthy dose of critical scepticism. While this is a message that may be difficult for many environmentalists to hear, the interests of sound public policy and decision making will surely be better served by taking it seriously.

5.4 Ten reasons why renewable energy technologies may not fully or directly replace fossil fuels

It is with this interest firmly in mind that we have endeavoured to apply the critical interpretation skills for which we advocate to our own engagement with the renewable energy transition knowledge base. Below we summarise the insights distilled through this engagement over many years. While we emphasise again our support for global transition to renewable energy systems, these are presented as 'ten reasons' why renewable energy sources and conversion technologies most likely cannot fully or directly replace the magnitude and nature of energy services provided by fossil fuels. These ten reasons comprise the eight matters explored in detail below, plus two additional 'meta-factors' considered in the subsequent discussion. These are not neatly discrete and independent matters. There is much overlap and interrelationship, apparent in the themes that recur throughout the presentation here.

In presenting the view that follows, we note also that in a world powered entirely by RE, the primary energy required to provide final energy services of the magnitude used in the non-energy economic sectors today will almost certainly reduce, and quite likely by a dramatic amount. This is because most final energy services today are provided via *thermal energy conversions*—for instance, electricity from thermal power stations and transport work using internal combustion engines. Thermal energy conversions necessarily involve dispersing in the order of 60–85% of the energy in the primary sources to the surrounding environment as heat. That heat is not available for the tasks that energy users want to perform. As such, current global primary energy use quite likely overstates by a significant margin the scale of the task that needs to be accomplished in a world where electricity from non-thermal energy conversions (including wind, PV and hydro) is the principal energy carrier.

Current global final energy use is a better guide, but the portion of this comprising transport fuels could also be expected to reduce significantly in a fully electrified world—once again, see the point above about current reliance of transport work on thermal energy conversions. On the other hand, if (as seems likely) transport remains significantly reliant on alternative liquid and gaseous fuels, and hence on thermal energy conversions, the difference may not be so great. For now we simply note that—as with so much of the energy transition landscape—this is an area subject to deep uncertainty.

Questions of this nature are ill-suited to resolution in the abstract via analytical techniques that are inherently prospective in nature. That is, where implementing the proposed changes that are under analysis would fundamentally alter the context for establishing the knowledge that the analysis itself relies upon.

This leaves aside for the moment the question of how the global energy sector's own demand for energy services might change in a fully electrified or 100% RE-powered world. As we discuss below, there is reason to expect that the scale of the energy services required for energy supply will increase significantly. Again though, uncertainties abound.

1. **'Theoretical potential' is not 'practically realisable potential'.** The conceptual nuance involved in the first point we make may at first glance seem rather abstract, but it has great practical significance. When people question the feasibility of fully replacing fossil fuels with renewable energy, one often hears in response that *of course* it is possible. After all, we know already how to convert the sun's energy into electricity, and merely one hour of sunlight striking Earth provides energy equivalent to a year's worth of human use. The sheer scale of solar energy's *theoretical potential* is so vast that many renewable advocates seem to assume that transitioning the global economy to renewables *must* therefore be perfectly feasible.[104] This assumption diverts attention from the more important question: what is the practically realisable potential of solar energy, after accounting for the full range of factors affecting its conversion to energy forms useful to human societies?

In considering the potential for renewable energy, there is a series of unavoidable 'discounts' applied to the earth energy flows that act as the primary sources from which human use is derived. To start with, there is a basic adjustment that needs to be made for geographical accessibility—most of the earth's surface is occupied by oceans, and a significant proportion of the remainder is glaciated or otherwise unsuited to large-scale energy capture and conversion. The naturally occurring energy flows that *are* accessible must then be converted via techniques for which the useful outputs entail inherent reductions relative to the inputs. This *technical potential* is governed by fundamental physical relations that are not subject to our influence, and is also mediated by practical technology-specific constraints.

The wider array of renewable energy sources without doubt holds promising potential, given that we already have the technical capacity to generate electricity via wind turbines, solar panels, biofuels, *et cetera*. But the proportion of this that can be realised in practice, once the broad spectrum of geographical, technical, engineering, environmental, economic and socio-political factors is taken into account, is far less certain—though certainly orders of magnitude less in absolute scale.

Here it's particularly important to appreciate that the practically realisable potential for RE is ultimately dependent on *engineered systems*. No matter the magnitude of the pool from which the final energy used by human systems is drawn, what is actually available for human use is a function of the scale of these engineered systems and the rates at which they can be deployed. The effort that is directed towards this engineering task—and the number of engineers allocated to it—has a major bearing on this. But engineers design systems within limits that pay little heed to abstract ideas about theoretical maxima. In most cases, such maxima merely delineate the outer bound between the world in which we actually live and fantasy. Engineers work with, but ultimately within, the performance characteristics, properties and availability of materials; the bounds of manufacturing techniques; the bounds of established transport, handling, and logistics infrastructures and institutions; the bounds of operability, maintainability and control; and so on.

Beyond this, the practical challenges of engineering systems for capturing, converting and distributing energy must be tackled within complex and encompassing socio-political contexts. This raises a raft of further questions. Will politicians be prepared to drive a renewables transition? Will vested interests (continue to) get in the way? Will cultural values adapt to accommodate higher energy prices? Will rural communities object to wind farms on aesthetic grounds? And so on. There are a thousand socio-political, economic and engineering reasons why the practically realisable potential of renewables will remain a fraction only of the technical potential. And this also illustrates why theoretical potential—the gross magnitudes of the various earth energy flows that act as the primary sources for RE conversions—is really only useful as a rule-of-thumb for estimating how best to distribute available capital across the various RE sources. Some of these broader contextual issues are unpacked further below. The point is, however, that we should not plan for a future where the best-case scenarios based on technical potential are treated as models for plausible futures—since they almost certainly will not be realised.[105]

2. **Intermittency, variability, base-load, dispatchability and cost.** When considering the prospects for transition to renewably powered economies, the intermittent and uncontrollably variable electricity supply provided by PV and wind looms large as the principal challenge that must be confronted. PV cells only produce electricity when the sun is shining; wind turbines only spin when the wind is blowing. On a calm night, therefore, renewable energy infrastructure reliant on these sources alone will generate no electricity.

But of course in today's industrial societies, demand for electricity will remain.[106] This contributes to what is sometimes referred to as the 'base-load problem', which arises as a consequence of the basic design characteristics of the steam-turbine power plants that provide the majority of electricity for most grids. These plants must be operated on a continuous basis at relatively constant output, and with a relatively high minimum output 'floor' below which they must be shut down altogether. It is these sources that supply the grid's minimum daily electricity demand, or 'base-load'.

In fact, in most cases they have come to dictate the *need for* and *level of* that minimum demand, as demand patterns have evolved to suit the supply-side requirement of continuous, steady-state operation. This base-load oriented demand pattern is subject to significant structural 'lock-in', due to the myriad social and economic habits and expectations that the availability of base-load power has given rise to. As such, there is a basic structural requirement, in the short term at the very least, that replacements for conventional steam-turbine thermal power generation provide equivalent dispatchability characteristics.[107] Hence the occurrence of the 'base-load problem' for grids highly reliant on generation sources that, by their very nature, cannot be considered as having the dispatchability characteristics of fossil fuel-powered generators.

The dispatchability problems that arise for grid systems dependent on intermittent and uncontrollably variable primary energy sources are more general, though, than the requirement to meet base-load demand. For instance, winter peaking grids, where demand is highest during winter evenings when the sun is not shining, present a particular challenge. Imagine a winter night when the wind is not blowing, in a region where fossil fuels have been phased out. People come home from work at 6pm, turn on the lights, television and heater, have a shower, bath the children, cook dinner, put on some washing. Electricity demand across an entire grid territory can peak at a time when solar is producing absolutely nothing. If the wind is also not blowing, where is the electricity supply coming from?

Sometimes the response is to note that the sun is always shining or the wind is always blowing *somewhere*. All we need to do to solve the issue is to distribute renewable electricity generation capacity sufficiently widely and then transmit that electricity to where it is needed. For example, Europe could just import electricity from the Sahara, as the Desertec project envisions. But to the extent that wider distribution of generating assets *can* actually increase supply reliability to a sufficient level, this has two major drawbacks. First, transmitting electricity long distances increases losses (reducing overall system efficiency and increasing costs). Second, and more significantly, this strategy requires replicating generation and transmission capacity across multiple regions (also increasing costs).[108] That would mean building infrastructure far beyond what is needed on 'good days' (i.e. days with simultaneously good sun and wind close to demand centres; days with moderate winds or low cloud cover across the entire grid territory).[109] On those good days, most of the infrastructure would be redundant, producing electricity that is not needed at that time.

A second response is simply to note that batteries or pumped hydro plants can store energy, which can be used later, when needed. That is, produce surplus electricity when the sun is shining and the wind is blowing, store it, and use that surplus to meet demand when it exceeds primary generation. This is technically feasible, but with major implications for overall cost of supply, even taking into account ongoing developments in battery technology and manufacturing.

The declining costs typically cited for wind and PV electricity— which certainly are promising—reflect the cost of supplying that electricity at the margins of grid systems. Here, the ability of grid systems to meet demand is underwritten by dispatchable capacity mainly reliant on fossil fuels. If the storage required to make intermittent RE sources similarly dispatchable is included (e.g. pumped hydro, batteries and hydrogen) then the economics change dramatically.

This is demonstrated by the price difference between grid-connected and off-grid household PV systems. Adding sufficient battery storage to cover a run of overcast days in mid-winter makes the system cost many times greater than a grid-connected PV system sized for the same average demand. Although this household example does not model the societal level challenge in all respects, the essential point remains: the economics of grid-connected PV (or wind) when integrated with fossil fuel dispatchable capacity is very different from PV (or wind) with sufficient storage to meet demand whenever it occurs.

The real issue here concerns the sheer scale of the storage challenge: even setting aside the major challenge of variation in solar irradiance between summer and winter, we are talking about storing energy for periods of days to weeks for entire countries. Suppose there is a calm and cloudy month in winter, when renewable generation is at a minimum. Such an extended period of unfavourable weather might only occur once every few years. But since industrial societies in their current forms are reliant on electricity supply being available on demand, it is these statistical outliers that determine the performance criteria for which supply systems must be designed.

The rapid reduction in price for lithium ion batteries is clearly having a big impact on the economics of electricity buffering, in both grid-connected and off-grid situations. But when we hear about 'major advances', 'plummeting prices' and 'booming deployment' in the context of popular media discourse, almost without exception this is relative to the existing installed base for RE generation and storage, rather than in relation to the macro-level physical economics of a global transition in all energy supply. Grid-connected batteries may prove to have very significant benefits for the stability of grids as the proportion of electricity generation from intermittent renewable sources increases, without significantly changing the situation with respect to long-term storage that we highlight here. The surge in media coverage relating to the favourable developments around battery technology really needs to be considered in this context. The practical benefits for grid management currently being realised as a consequence of battery technology and manufacturing developments relate to a class of problems quite distinct from the far larger challenge of long-term energy storage.

If the response to this challenge is to say that coal, gas or biomass can 'fill the gaps' on these rare occasions without relying exclusively on storage, then the economic problem of replicating plant and infrastructure, with associated high costs, again arises. This particular issue really demands a book-length treatment in its own right. The technical literature is complex and often riddled with controversy, and we cannot do justice to all the intricacies. For instance, the local context has a major bearing on the prospects for different renewable sources and conversion technologies in different regions. Most of Norway's electricity comes from hydroelectricity, a vastly different situation to the world considered as a whole. Iceland's geothermal resource makes its situation similarly unique. And the prospects for PV electricity are far more favourable in Australia, with its abundance of intense sunlight, than in the UK or Japan. Our present point, again, is that from a global perspective, running societies on 100% renewable energy is likely to be more difficult and costly than typically assumed, providing another compelling reason to reduce energy demand rather than merely trying to green the supply.

The storage challenge gets comparatively easier as electricity demand reduces and becomes more flexible. We will now emphasise, however, that if intermittency and uncontrollable variability proves to be a challenge as electricity supply transitions to renewable generation, the challenge only compounds when thinking through the prospects of decarbonising the entire global energy system with renewables. As we will see, transport presents a particular conundrum.

3. **Electricity is only 18% of global final energy demand.** As noted earlier, the key RE technologies of solar, wind and hydro

produce electricity, but electricity is only 18% of global final energy demand. Even if tomorrow electricity supply suddenly became 100% renewable, the challenge of providing the services enabled by the other 82% of final energy would remain.[110] The task of satisfying electricity demand from predominantly intermittent renewable sources is difficult and expensive even when this is less than one fifth of the global final energy supply task. Imagine then the magnitude of the challenge if all or almost all energy demand is to be met with electricity from a similar mix of sources.

It is, of course, theoretically conceivable that today's oil-dependent global transport systems come to run on electricity (or synthetic fuels produced using electricity) instead of oil, and that other key oil-intensive tasks, like mining and agriculture, do the same. And it is theoretically conceivable that such a society also builds such vast energy storage systems that it can still meet energy demand over a few weeks of overcast and calm weather when the RE infrastructure is barely producing. But again, theoretical potential and practically realisable potential are two very different things. Solving this liquid fuels problem appears to be the greatest challenge to creating post-carbon societies.

What are the prospects of converting the energy services dependent on today's 95 Mbpd of oil consumption to renewable electricity? Currently electric vehicles (EVs) make up only 0.2% (or 2 million) of the global fleet (of around 1 billion). In 2017 the IEA reported that even if EVs scaled up to 280 million by 2040 this would only make a 1% difference to carbon emissions given the expected carbon intensity of electricity at that time.[111] The prospect of creating electric passenger planes suitable for allowing commercial aviation to continue on its current scale is negligible. The biophysical economic constraints to running commercial aviation on biofuels suggest that biofuel air transport will at best play an extremely minor role on the path to decarbonisation (more on biofuels below). Running global mining operations solely or mostly on electricity (whether renewably generated or not) seems similarly implausible, as does any hope of transitioning to a global fleet of electric cargo trucks.[112]

It is one thing to accept that converting energy services from fossil fuels to renewable electricity is a critical goal in any post-carbon strategy. It seems near delusional, though, to expect that it will be possible to run a global post-carbon civilisation, functionally equivalent to the world with which we're familiar today, on 100% renewable energy.

4. **Biofuels?** If the transition to a post-carbon civilisation hinges primarily on addressing the liquid fuels challenge, and if electric vehicles alone are unable to decarbonise a growing fleet of cars, trucks, planes, ships and heavy equipment, then sometimes biofuels are held up as the solution. We know how to make liquid fuels from plants, such as biodiesel from wide ranging feedstocks, and ethanol from corn, sugar cane or algae. So perhaps we simply need to scale up production?

This approach might sound plausible in theory but again the difference between theoretical potential and practically realisable potential is vast. The prime obstacle to scaling up biofuels is the land and resources (or, in the case of algal biofuels, impacts on marine environment) needed to do so. We live in a world where global population is approaching eight billion people, many of whom today go hungry, with the population trending toward eleven billion by the end of the century. Food security is already a serious problem today and will get more challenging as the population grows. Available arable land is finite—the more land and resources dedicated to biofuels, the less there is for food production. There is also the risk that expanding biofuel production will drive yet more deforestation.

For present purposes, the final key limitation of biofuels is their typically low EROI—generally less than 5:1 and sometimes closer to 1:1. A world in which transport is powered by biofuels would require a vastly expanded fuels supply infrastructure, with attendant economic implications. Clearly this is a poor energy replacement for the 17:1 oil that is available today. With current global biofuel production less than 2% of annual world oil production, the prospects for significant scale-up seem dim. Biofuels are sure to play important niche roles in post-carbon societies, but the overall scale of the contribution is likely to be very limited relative to liquid fuel use today.[113]

5. **Renewable technologies rely on fossil fuels.** We've been using the language of '100% renewable energy' to represent a transition to wind, solar, hydro and biofuels *et cetera*. But there is a disconcerting problem underlying such a shift that is often glossed over: currently the availability of RE interception and conversion technologies—their manufacture, deployment, operation, maintenance and end-of-life management—is inextricably dependent on the fossil fuels that it's hoped they will replace. This has even led some investigators to conclude that wind and solar electricity are not so much fossil fuel *replacements* as they are fossil fuel 'extenders'. By adding energy (with zero operational fuel input) at the margins of an electricity grid system, they reduce the average fuel input per unit of electricity delivered by the grid system as a whole. But the renewable generators remain reliant on the existing grid to give value to the electrical energy that they contribute.[114] And this is just the system operability issue. Consider the intricately ramified picture that emerges on tracing the myriad ways that fossil fuels enable the very supply chains through which wind turbines and PV equipment come to be deployed in the first place.

Reflect for a moment on what it takes for just a single large wind turbine to exist. The materials with which it is embodied were mined and processed with oil-dependent machinery; its components were transported by ships and heavy haulage vehicles; once erected it is held in place by massive—thousands of tonnes for the largest models—concrete foundations. These machines, the scale of which can inspire awe, might be viewed as amongst the pre-eminent and definitive expressions of carbon civilisation at its peak. Consider then that a transition to a global energy system based entirely on renewably generated electricity may require, according to one estimate, the deployment of approximately 2.5 million such turbines, plus 87,000 square kilometres of rooftop solar panels, and 260,000 square kilometres of ground-based solar PV and concentrated solar thermal collectors.[115] Today there is not a single solar panel or wind turbine that was not dependent on fossil fuels for its manufacture and throughout its supply chain. For the foreseeable future, at the very least, the deployment of RE infrastructure will remain locked via innumerable path dependencies to the fossil-fuelled industrial world that humanity has built over the past three centuries. It is theoretically conceivable that in the future all the processes involved in RE supply system production—including mining, manufacture and transport—can be powered by renewably generated electricity. But between present reality and the realisation of such a vision lies a vast landscape of engineering, economic and institutional challenges that humanity has hardly begun to confront.

This is no argument against as rapid a deployment of RE technology as humanity can mobilise. Instead, it is a further argument for creating societies that require as little energy as possible to flourish, rather than assuming that energy-intensive societies can simply transition to RE technologies without difficulty.

6. **Energy return on investment.** The implications of energy return on investment (EROI) for RE transition feasibility is a vexed and often highly contentious area of inquiry. The EROI for an energy supply technology is highly context specific, and it is not possible to arrive at definitive assessments of EROI that apply to all situations.[116] Nonetheless, some general observations can be made about EROI of wind and PV electricity relative to incumbent energy sources, and how this relates to questions

about the forms that future societies may take.

Firstly, it is axiomatic that adding energy storage, increased transmission and distribution, and redundant supply capacity to existing systems entails significant energy costs and hence reduces EROI at the overall system level. This can be mitigated only to the extent that technology change and efficiency improvements offset these increasing system-level energy costs. Secondly, to the extent that RE systems remain dependent on a globally integrated industrial economy dependent on fossil fuels (as we argue in 5 above), then declining EROI of fossil fuels (discussed previously in Chapter 3, Section 3.1) will feed through into declining EROI of these systems.

Following from this, a question arises as to what declining EROI implies for the viability of consumption- and growth-oriented industrial economies. As EROI declines, the proportion of total available energy services that must be directed towards the overall economy's energy supply sub-system increases. If overall supply of energy services cannot expand fast enough to compensate, then this implies reducing energy service availability for all other economic activity enabled by the energy sub-system. In such a situation, the strong dependence of economic activity on sufficient energy services implies a contraction in the rest of the physical economy.[117]

A situation such as this would be exacerbated in the transition phase to RE, as the energy investment in transitioning supply systems to renewable sources represents an additional drain on available energy services. The required energy investment rate is particularly sensitive to the rate of transition. Wind and PV electricity supply systems require relatively large proportions of their energy investment upfront, before they deliver useful outputs, increasing the sensitivity to transition rate. The higher the transition rate, the greater the diversion of energy services from the rest of the economy to the energy sector.

Attention at this point often turns to the question of the minimum EROI required to support societies functionally equivalent to today's. Again though, trying to pin down a definitive answer to this may be something of a distraction. What any social form ultimately requires in order to remain viable, in energetic terms, is that the necessary forms of energy services be available at sufficient *rates*. In principle, so long as the energy sector delivers more energy over its lifecycle than it uses for that task (i.e. EROI > 1), then viability is dependent on having sufficient *power* availability at any given instant in time. But EROI is specifically defined over the full lifecycle of an asset. Even if a supply system comprises assets with EROI much greater than 1 over their operating lives, the power return ratio (the *rate* of energy return over the *rate* at which energy is used to provide the return) for the system as a whole at a given instant in time can be far lower, even less than 1.

Ultimately, the viability of a society from an energy perspective depends on its ability to meet the ongoing costs (financial, environmental, material *and* energetic) of providing sufficient power at any given point in time. Energy-focused lifecycle assessment is clearly essential for understanding the long-term prospects of any social form, and hence for assessing the feasibility of transitions to 100% RE. But at the whole-of-society level for which such assessment must be conducted, it is power return ratios that are most directly relevant.

Transition from fossil fuelled societies to societies powered by 100% RE, at least on the multi-decadal timeframes that are typically discussed by proponents, will almost certainly constrain the power available to non-energy supply economic sectors. To enable such transition, economies and the societies that they support will need to adapt accordingly.

7. **Power density.** The spatial intensity of energy use is often overlooked in assessing the prospects for renewably powered societies, but is critically important. This spatial intensity is most

readily measured via *power density*, typically the rate of energy use or supply per unit of horizontal land area occupied by the systems involved.[118]

The reason this is so important is that while the power densities achieved by incumbent supply systems typically exceed the power densities at which energy is used in urban industrial societies, for RE this relationship between power density of supply and use is reversed. In fact with power densities ranging from roughly 1 W/m^2 (wind) to a few tens of watts per square metre (PV), RE supply power density is orders of magnitude lower than peak usage rates for industrial plants and high-rise buildings (often greater than 1000 W/m^2), and lower even than average rates over city centres (in the order of 500 W/m^2). Even energy use power densities averaged over *entire* city areas (including low-density suburbs) can be several times higher than maximum power densities for best-case PV supply.

Consequently, a transition to energy systems dominated by renewable sources will see a shift from energy supply occupying much smaller areas than those over which it is used, to one in which human settlements depend on hinterlands many times their size to capture and concentrate the energy that they use. Without vast reductions in power density of energy use, there is essentially no prospect that urban densification and local energy self-sufficiency will coexist. Such self-sufficiency will be possible only where demand expectations are reduced, and density of habitation is sufficiently low. Where local climate conditions are favourable, suburban population densities probably represent the upper limit for household or neighbourhood energy self-sufficiency.

This presents a major challenge in a world characterised by an almost universal ongoing trajectory in the direction of urban densification. It certainly means that a shift to energy supply dominated by RE will also mean high reliance on utility-scale systems, and an increased rather than decreased reliance on grid interconnectivity, even if the grids in question only bear passing resemblance to those familiar today. On the other hand, a reversal in the densification of human settlements could very well be accompanied by a shift towards greater local energy self-sufficiency. Either way, there are major implications for the forms of human settlements and the institutional arrangements by which they are organised. The disruptions, and potential *ruptures*, entailed here stand to be significantly ameliorated by energy demand reductions realised through coordinated social change processes, rather than by reactive emergency response to crisis conditions.

8. **Energy system transitions are slow and complicated.** The experience of accelerating technological change, particularly in relation to computing and information technology, but also in the renewable energy area itself, drives a widespread perception that a transition to 100% RE can occur on a timeframe of a few decades. Some pundits even tout the plausibility of achieving this in a single decade. Such hopes are strongly at odds with the record of historical energy transitions.[119] These have typically occurred over timeframes on the order of a century or more— and none have involved the scope and scale of change involved in shifting *en masse* to renewable energy. This is because past transitions, even with the large-scale expansion of coal use, have tended to involve expansion of total supply by adding new energy sources to the existing base. What is now envisaged with large-scale RE transition involves substituting incumbent sources with alternatives—swapping horses mid-stream, so to speak. For RE to replace rather than just extend fossil fuels, fossil-fuelled supply capacity will need to be retired as RE capacity is rolled out. This is a far more institutionally, infrastructurally and logistically complex challenge than expanding existing capacity by adding RE at the margins of the fossil-fuelled system.

As we have noted, rapid transition can have significant implications for energy service availability for the rest of the economy. Retiring existing assets in parallel only exacerbates this. This may also have significant carbon emission implications, if the politically expedient response to such an energy cannibalising effect is to reverse previous actions, for example by recommissioning mothballed fossil fuel plants.[120]

In addition to these eight points, we also recognise two 'meta-factors' that constrain the potential for humanity to do via RE what it currently does via its incumbent energy systems. Turning to the first of these, we make the general observation that RE technology is dependent on a wide range of mineral resources for which a major transition effort will have significant implications for overall demand. That is, supply-demand dynamics for those resources stand to be significantly affected by the transition rate. This can be expected to drive environmental and resource use 'problem shifting', whereby addressing one set of challenges leads to new problems in other areas.[121] At just the time humanity is encountering the limits of its dominant ways of organising societies and economies, the transition to RE calls for doing *more*— in fact much more—of what got us into this predicament in the first place. More work, more physical production, and a great deal more engineering, manufacturing and construction. Engineered systems are implicated at some point in just about every joule of human energy use. This engineering effort entails major costs, measurable in financial, environmental and resource terms. The increased engineering effort required for RE transition translates into increases in all of these.

Here we have attempted to set out the case for why powering societies functionally equivalent to those familiar to us today entirely (or almost so) via RE faces major obstacles. As we have argued throughout, unpacking this question of renewable energy's capacity to meet humanity's demand for energy services depends a great deal on the *level* of that demand. Here we need to consider what is needed, in terms of energy services, to live in the ways that humans are content to live. The nature of the envisaged transition means that we are entering entirely unexplored territory, and the pathways that we walk into existence are subject to inherent, irreducible uncertainty. It is impossible to know upfront just how these pathways will unfold, the full range of challenges that will be encountered along the way, and where the novel responses to them will take us. As such, there is very good reason to think that the situations that emerge will be very different from the expectations created by any model constructed or plan conceived today.

We believe that the situation we have outlined here infers the need for a high degree of 'knowledge humility' in approaching energy transition questions. It's our view that the prospects for good outcomes—outcomes in which we humans find ways of living well together that have long-term viability—will be greatly assisted by acknowledging that even the best available evidence today leaves many questions open and in need of continued inquiry.

This case for humility can only be emphasised further when one looks at the real world to see how far the renewable energy transition has advanced in recent decades. The world knew enough about fossil fuels and climate change in 1988 to establish the IPCC, so in the last thirty years, what progress has been made on renewables? In December 2017, the IEA published its annual *Key World Energy Statistics* and reported that wind, solar and geothermal together provide merely 1.5% of global primary energy supply. Given the importance of a renewable transition, this statistic might tempt one to despair. But, of course, despair will not help, just as green illusions about the ease of a 100% renewable energy transition will not help. We need to be informed by reality—confronting though it can be—and act on that basis. And that means recognising that a transition to 100% renewable energy is going to be more difficult, slower and almost certainly more expensive than most people hope will be the case.

So next time someone says that one hour of sunlight can power the global economy for a year, and that solar panels are cheaper than coal, ask them to reflect on the state of the transition to date. The greater the demand for energy services, the lower the likelihood that RE can meet that demand. As demand expectations decrease, the likelihood increases. The practical point, with respect to energy-intensive societies, is that it would be better to organise and prepare for reduced energy demand (i.e. energy descent), because the less energy we need, the easier any transition to 100% renewable energy will be.

The second 'meta-factor', rounding out our 'ten reasons' for seeing it as highly unlikely that renewable energy will replace fossil fuels in any direct sense, enters the picture here. In short, the machinations of political economy will win out: if such a transition is long, difficult and expensive (in financial, resource and a host of other terms), as we believe it will be, then systems of human organisation and their environments will evolve together accordingly in a manner that conserves their mutual adaptation. Whatever forms this takes will very likely entail reduced *availability of*, and hence *demand for*, energy services. In physical terms, less work, heating and lighting—and so energy will be intercepted from the environment and converted to forms useful to human systems at rates far lower than for incumbent sources.

Again we stress that our analysis should in no way be interpreted as 'anti-renewable energy'. We have taken pains to clarify that it is our desire for a world run primarily or wholly on renewable energy as soon as possible. But given the many limitations of renewable energy when compared with performance criteria set by and peculiar to incumbent energy sources, we have argued that any such transition will mean significantly reduced energy services compared to industrially advanced societies today. And it is not only the *magnitude* of services available that is likely to reduce, which itself will have deep socio-economic implications. The *nature* of the services made available by renewable energy systems will be sufficiently different to those provided by incumbent supply systems that a post-carbon society will likely need to undergo fundamental changes and adaptations in its economic, political, social and cultural characteristics.

Chapter 6. Navigation Notes for Energy Descent Futures

So far we have not attempted to describe the range of preparatory or adaptive strategies that are available for dealing with energy descent; nor have we discussed in any detail what a post-carbon civilisation might look like. Our goal has been diagnostic rather than prescriptive. That said, we believe the diagnosis supports the case for, and adaptive potential of, engaging intentionally with energy descent processes. Drawing attention to this perspective is important because until the plausibility of such energy futures is understood and taken seriously, individuals, communities and political processes will not be mobilised to prepare for their eventuality. A range of looming energy shocks may well arrive and societies will be unprepared for them, which is likely to bring unnecessary suffering, harm and instability. At the extreme, it potentially precipitates civilisational collapse. In light of this, before closing we will say a few words on the cultural and socio-economic implications of energy descent, and the variety of responses available. The brief overview we present can only anticipate the much more extensive discussion that the subject both requires and deserves.[122]

In earlier chapters we discussed the ways in which energy surpluses are used by societies to solve the problems they encounter, and typically also to feed growing and evolving material desires. We showed that as societies acquire and invest energy to solve problems and feed desires, they become more socio-politically complex (in the social scientific sense, of increasing social role differentiation and specialisation, with attendant expansion of the means for coordinating these roles; this tends also to be accompanied by expanded suites of technologies and related institutions—see our extended endnote relating to this choice of terminology[123]). This in turn drives the need for further complexification, and hence increased energy use. Because existential problems are in fact being solved, it is widely inferred that such a trajectory of change represents a general progressive improvement in life conditions within a complexifying society—for the time being at least.[124]

As an aside, we stress here that we do not subscribe to the view that increasing socio-political complexification constitutes a trajectory of *general* progress or improvement. We distinguish this idea of general progress from the ongoing possibility—which we *do* subscribe to—of localised performance improvement in specific contexts, as measured by appropriately defined and context-specific criteria. Human history is not in our interpretation characterised by a unidirectional, largely deterministic and hence predictable pattern of change from less to more socially desirable states.[125] We just point out that this is an interpretation that is widely held and that is a highly influential cultural characteristic of modernity.

Economic growth is one prominent area of performance from which a general trajectory of progress is often inferred. Money and other financial assets—the instruments that mediate economic activity— can be viewed as claims on the product of surplus energy. Societies allocate money to initiatives intended to solve their problems, and the expansion of physical economic activity that this stimulates and incentivises entails increased rates of energy use. As discussed earlier, this energy-economy relationship is evidenced historically by the close correlation between economic activity measured in terms of GDP and total primary energy use. Provided energy surpluses continue to grow, economies have been able to grow in scale and socio- political complexity. On the surface, then, it is quite understandable why more money and energy are overriding goals of most, if not all, contemporary economies: these are apparently required for maintaining the conditions that are interpreted as 'progress', and that, as such, are widely attributed the status of being of ultimate value.

But what happens (or might happen in future) when a society finds itself with less energy to invest in economic growth, and the socio-political complexification growth both brings and requires? There are two broad pathways it may follow: either it tries to maintain the existing, growth-oriented socio-economic form but solve fewer problems due to the declining energy budget (a phenomenon typically characterisable as societal decay, recession or collapse, depending on the speed and extent of decline); or the society rethinks the range and nature of the problems it is willing to solve, and then reprioritises its investment of available energy in order to create new, less energy intensive socio-political and economic forms.

It seems clear enough that rich nations (our focus herein) are in the process of choosing the former strategy—evidenced by their unremitting hunger for more energy, more (and more diverse) technological solutions and more economic growth. This dominant strategy is selected on the assumption that more energy will be available in the future to fund the attendant increase in socio-political complexity. This is the message relentlessly pushed by mainstream energy analysts and institutions. However, the central implication of our analysis is that it would be prudent to embrace the radical alternative strategies of voluntary simplification (of the socio-political structures for organising human activity) and economic deintensification, given the likelihood of forthcoming energy descent.[126] What, then, might such voluntary simplification look like? We sketch a view here in the broadest possible terms, and we expect to raise as many new questions as we answer.

Given that sufficient rates of energy supply in appropriate forms are required for production activity within a given socio-political-economic complex, it follows that in an energy descent context voluntary simplification would involve less overall production activity in physical terms, which would also mean less material- and energy-intensive consumption. From an engineering perspective, this decline in production activity is a simple consequence of less overall work and heat transfer being carried out by a society's physical plant, equipment and infrastructure.[127] Today the outcome of this process of organised economic contraction widely goes by the name 'degrowth' (which for present purposes can be considered a consequence of success in the positive development of voluntarily simplified societies and deintensified economies). But degrowth does not merely mean less of the same type of economic activity within the same system; it also means less and different, within a new system. Depending on local context: not simply fewer SUVs, but more bikes (or less desire for transit in the first place); not just less deforestation but more reforestation; not fewer meals in the day, but different diets; and so forth, across all domains of life. In other words, not the same narratives of human identity, success and wellbeing, but new narratives of what it means to be human.

Within such new narratives, if the social justice imperative of meeting the basic wants[128] of all people were to be realised, the reduced material output of economic activity in a degrowth transition would need to be distributed more fairly than it is in most societies today. In other words, the degrowth economies would not be structured to maximise economic growth and hope that wealth 'trickles down'; instead the economies we envisage here should ensure material sufficiency for all more directly, through the creation of new distributive ground rules that do not rely on growth. Here the same social 'problem' is solved, only in alternative, less energy and resource intensive ways, which is a key feature of what we mean by voluntary simplification.

This process of shrinking or abandoning many present economic arrangements in organised ways should not be assumed to automatically imply social hardship or deprivation, provided communities negotiate the transition mindfully. And although significant deindustrialisation would ensue, obviously some economic sectors would expand in order to meet real and ongoing human desires in regenerative and equitable ways (notably RE infrastructure). Granted, consumer affluence as we know it today may not be viable for any or many—clearly requiring a fundamental shift in cultures of consumption and conceptions of the 'good life'. But once basic material wants were met and appropriate technologies developed, degrowth societies would have the freedom to turn away from limitless material advancement and instead seek happiness and meaning in life through less consumptive avenues—where, as it happens, pretty much every wisdom and spiritual tradition advises that lasting fulfilment lies.[129]

Members of post-consumerist cultures enabled by voluntary simplification would thus have increased scope to choose the realm of the spirit, not the shopping mall, to satisfy their hunger for contentment. Paradoxically, the shift to less consumptive pursuits might imply not an outright *rejection* of material culture but a 'new materialism', in which post-materialist cultures actually pay more attention to and exercise greater care for the material realm (e.g. building things to last and taking care of them). This might be motivated by highly utilitarian concerns, such as minimising environmental impacts or resource extraction and discarding of waste. But it can also be consistent with what might be termed spiritual motivations, a move to healing or transcending the supposed enmities between 'culture and nature' and 'body and mind'.

The degrowth in production and consumption required by energy descent is one thing. But as noted earlier, it is not just the *magnitude* of energy availability that shapes a society. It is also the *nature* of the energy sources, especially their power density. Assuming that a degrowth society is fully or primarily powered by renewable energy, with little or no use of fossil energy and a limited role for nuclear electricity, it follows that such a society would have to adapt to the fundamentally different nature of energy supply, as well as reduced overall availability. In order to avoid an economically crippling reliance on expensive energy storage, a degrowth society may need to adjust by storing *work*, using energy as far as possible when the sun is shining or the wind is blowing, rather than assuming that energy is always available on demand and without interruption. While modest biofuel volumes could be produced for tasks deemed socially essential (such as limited use of heavy machinery and aviation), a defining feature of a post-carbon society would be the electrification of essential energy-demanding tools and technologies and even a return to human-labour power for more tasks (including farming). Overall, of course, energy demand would have to be significantly reduced compared to rich nations today. Precise levels, though, are subject to the myriad social, political, economic, technological and cultural characteristics of as-yet-unknown viable human futures.

In short, degrowth processes of voluntary simplification, as we envisage them, would seek to meet genuine human wants and essential needs in sustainable ways through socio-economic practices that are far less energy and resource intensive than in industrially advanced societies today. As well as a range of institutional and structural changes (which we won't attempt to review here), such degrowth societies would have to be shaped by values of material sufficiency, moderation and frugality—simply because there would be insufficient surplus energy to meet the energy (or broader environmental) costs of consumer lifestyles.

Central to the changes we see as plausibly enabling this is a decrease in hours spent working in the formal economy. This would free up increased time for participation in the informal economy at the household and community levels. In such a world, repair, recycling and reuse would be radically embraced and practised, incentivised by the increased value of materials. Clothes might be second-hand, mended or produced within the household and neighbourhood economies. Cultures based on rapid fashion cycles would very likely wither away and new aesthetics of sufficiency and timeless classic design might emerge. Home energy use would have to be a fraction of typical usage in rich societies but homes would be retrofitted for energy efficiency and essential functions could be met. Permaculture gardens and food forests would reshape the urban and suburban landscapes. Car culture would enter its terminal phase as oil becomes ever-scarcer, and bicycles and public transport would become primary modes of transit.[130] Regular air travel would become unaffordable, as would consumer lifestyles more generally. Infrastructure that is currently replicated across all households would increasingly be shared at the neighbourhood scale. Food and other commodities would generally be grown, produced and traded far more locally than at present. Markets local to living places could be expected to proliferate to facilitate this trade.[131]

This rough and incomplete thumbnail sketch seeks simply to highlight how a degrowth process of voluntary simplification points towards non-affluent but sufficient material living standards. By avoiding the energy inputs currently invested in the vast mediating economic structures necessary to support large-scale societies oriented towards continuous and unchecked growth, degrowth societies would thereby still have sufficient energy available to meet wants consistent with human flourishing.

Approached judiciously and with appropriate care, we see it as entirely conceivable that sufficient surplus energy would also be available to allow continued collective problem-solving on a significant scale. But problems would be solved in ways different to those that have become habitual during the industrial age. Different value-systems would even produce different conceptions of the problems faced and, with this, new ways of thinking about the nature of adequate solutions.

This has potentially profound implications for the nature of legitimate knowledge and praxis in societies shaped by processes of economic deintensification. In Chapter 5, we emphasised the crucial role of engineering and engineers in the global-scale transition of energy systems, and by implication—given the ubiquity of engineered energy conversions in *all* economic activity—of essentially all technologically-mediated human endeavours. In thinking about what it might take for societies to deintensify in ways and to extents called for as they evolve within degrowth contexts necessitated by energy descent, we believe a different emphasis is now called for. The type of expert-driven technical know-how, of which the engineering way of sense-making is perhaps *the* preeminent species, is fundamentally and inextricably implicated in the genesis of the dilemma with which humanity now must grapple. In trying to craft viable response pathways, to rely principally on this way of sense-making, or to elevate its privileged status further, could be expected to exacerbate the dysfunctions that it is hoped such responding will ameliorate. The situation humanity finds itself in calls for seeing, knowing, acting and being that differs qualitatively from this.

This is not to deny the necessary role of technology and engineering in navigating viable energy descent pathways, it is only to emphasise that a techno-fix alone will be insufficient if not set within a suitable framework of reappraised values. Technologies are tools the use of which is inevitably shaped by the cultural contexts in which they are deployed.

We see this as necessarily requiring the engagement of full-spectrum citizenries, and this in turn calls for a radical democratisation of the knowledge and praxis that is most socially valued. The knowledge practices needed in order for human societies to emerge that are characterised by continuous mutual learning[132] oriented towards the regeneration of their enabling contexts, will be practices in which all can participate, and that are simultaneously open to the knowledges with which all prospective participants show up. By drawing the application and deployment of specialist technical knowledges within the contextual fold of a socially-embodied orientation that might be characterised as *regenerative mutual learning*, the tiny minority of expert practitioners who by default call so many of the shots in contemporary industrial societies might be relieved of some of the burden of responsibility that they now bear in often-lonely isolation. This unweighting stands to open rich reservoirs of latent creative potential, as new priorities and cares reorient collective sense-making and acting.

Reflecting (and enacted via) knowledge practices with such qualities, how voluntary simplification unfolds in practice could take an essentially infinite number of forms. It defies precise forecasting. Indeed, the shape of a flourishing degrowth society in an energy descent context is limited only by its members' shared imagination. Scarcity begets creativity. Voluntary simplification is based on an essentially *polycultural* vision, as distinct from modernity's *monocultural* vision. This is a vision where the trajectory of change will involve many of infinite possible social forms being enacted simultaneously, in response to local conditions. This diversity will be amplified by the interactions between groups pursuing viable trajectories free of the constraints of uniformity imposed by massive bureaucracies and centralised institutions. In important respects, as David Fleming has pointed out, this 'simplification' in fact entails a drift to greater complexity. Again, this is simplification only in the limited sense of reduction in the formal socio-political complexity— that is, institutionalised social role differentiation and diversification, and attendant means of coordination—that characterises large-scale societies.[133]

Obviously, such 'simplification' of past socio-political complexity will be experienced very differently if it is chaotically imposed upon a society as a consequence of collapse, instead of being creatively and caringly navigated into existence through deliberate intention. Degrowth by way of voluntary simplification and economic deintensification provides not just an alternative to collapse, but also the potential for prosperous descent.

Nevertheless, no matter how well justified degrowth may be as a coherent response to global crises, we again acknowledge that it seems unlikely to be widely embraced by governments or civil societies. But this does not undermine the case for degrowth. If, in the face of the evidence, nations continue to pursue economic growth without end, and thereby continue to collide with ecological limits, then we argue that degrowth values and practices remain justified as a means of building resilience to forthcoming shocks. In other words, we should aim for regenerative forms of social organisation that build rather than deplete the foundations on which they rely.

Chapter 7. Constituting the Future

We set out to show through this critical exploration that much mainstream energy discourse is based on a series of highly optimistic assumptions about future energy supply. The improbability of conditions aligning such that all necessary assumptions are born out implies that the energy futures ahead will diverge strongly from those envisaged within this established discourse. This has potentially profound implications. The availability of energy in the right forms at sufficient rates is the lifeblood of any particular form of civilisation. Energy-related factors are fundamental to how we shape our societies and pursue our goals—yet it seems most individuals and societies are making plans based on highly implausible expectations. In this book, we've encouraged readers to treat the prospect that these expectations will *not* be realised as, at the very least, a matter of *plausibility*. At this juncture though, we wish to state very clearly that, by our interpretation, the evidence presently available indicates that an energy descent future, in some form, is extremely likely and should in fact be approached as a matter of *inevitability*.

In the event that mainstream expectations are thwarted, the consequences could range from the disruptive to the catastrophic. This is not a case *against* optimism, but rather of channelling it in directions that lie within humanity's scope of influence. Even within the difficult circumstances that our assessment implies, there is still much good that can be achieved. Ample room remains for adjusting expectations to better reflect underlying energy and environmental realities, and to reconstitute societies—and the economies that support them—accordingly.

Our critique focussed on three key issues: (1) the likelihood (or unlikelihood) of meeting growing energy demand as fossil fuels continue to deplete; (2) the size of the available carbon budget for a safe climate and the economic implications of keeping within such a budget; and (3) the degree to which alternative energy sources (renewables and/or nuclear) will be able to replace the fossil energy foundations of carbon civilisation, without significant disruption to today's large-scale societies and the dominant political-economic paradigm of global market capitalism.

We argued that the peak oil phenomenon is not dead but at most in short term remission. Ongoing fossil energy depletion is likely to cause supply disruptions in coming years and decades and thereby undermine the energy supply needed to maintain economic growth. In any case, we showed that the carbon budget for a safe climate is so tight (and in fact is arguably non-existent) that decarbonising at the rate needed is inconsistent with ongoing economic growth. This means we should be choosing to leave fossil fuels even before they leave us. But as we argued, that requires the unthinkable: transcending the growth imperative that is common to all large-scale societies but which is greatly amplified within competitive economies operating under market capitalism.

Finally, we looked beneath the gloss of promising advancements in energy sources and conversion technologies, showing that alternative energy sources differ dramatically in nature from incumbent sources (intermittency, storage issues, low energy density, system cost, etc.). Considered systemically, these differences imply that the alternatives will not directly replace the fossil energy foundations of carbon civilisation. In short, we have argued that a post-carbon civilisation is most likely to be one with less energy available, not more, and hence with reduced energy *services* in the form of work, heat, lighting and data manipulation than is currently available in rich nations. The situation is compounded if distributive questions are taken seriously. Ultimately, this means it would be prudent to be planning for energy descent futures.

In closing, we appreciate the psychological drivers for denying these conclusions and trusting instead in a cornucopian or techno-optimistic worldview. It is less confronting to human identities and ways of life to believe that technology and markets can solve social and environmental problems without needing to rethink the underpinning structures that give rise to those problems. We posit that this means of coping with psychological dissonance, perhaps adaptive in other circumstances, is influential in the apparent 'self-censoring' (consciously or unconsciously) by mainstream energy and economic analysts, resulting in the publication only of perspectives consistent with dominant economic and political paradigms.[134] But critical, evidence-based thinking demands that we should not believe something merely because we wish it to be so. In our view, it is preferable to believe and act upon what is most likely to be true following an honest and frank weighing of the evidence. We have argued that this means accepting more modest visions of future access to energy services and creatively preparing for the socio-economic implications of energy descent.

The age of energy abundance is drawing to an end. Perhaps it has already ended. We have created a form of carbon civilisation the energy demands of which cannot be sustainably or fairly maintained. Certainly, this high-consumption, energy-intensive way of life cannot be globalised to the entire, growing population approaching eight billion. As Joseph Tainter maintains: 'a society or other institution can be destroyed by the cost of sustaining itself.'[135] Our message, therefore, is to accept the implied energy descent futures before their consequences overwhelm us. This is likely to be an extremely challenging and uncertain journey. But it also has the potential to offer people renewed prospects for lives of meaning and purpose, provided we learn to collectively see these overlapping crises as opportunities for deep civilisational transformation.

The human opportunity, as always, is to constitute the future rather than be constituted by it. Today that requires seeing through the dubious and even dangerous optimism of energy cornucopianism and developing an appreciation of, and even *desire for*, futures of the kind that energy descent entails. We acknowledge that this prospect will be interpreted by many as carrying associations of deprivation and defeat, and thus seem undesirable. Consider a metaphor though. For a pilot nearing the range limit of their aircraft's fuel supply, making a controlled descent in order to land safely is so natural and expected that the plane passing overhead is barely registered. It is only in the rare instance in which a pilot, in error or incapacitated, acts contrary to their passengers' and their own interests, crashing to the ground with great violence, that such an everyday occurrence as the end of an aircraft's flight suddenly galvanises collective attention. Dystopian interpretations of descent are not inherent in the concept itself. Rather, they are an entailment of cultural priorities formed around the present civilisation's dominant story of progress.

Given that the energy prospects of the old story are beginning to fade, we find ourselves in a sort of limbo, in between stories. What is required today more than anything else is a new story. Or rather, an assemblage of new stories, which together help us break through the thick crust of conventional thinking and being, thus allowing us to think and be otherwise, as pioneering citizens of a post-carbon civilisation, in a world not yet made.

Glossary

Barrel	Commonly used volumetric unit for quantifying oil production and consumption, equal to 158.987 litres.
Conventional oil (and gas)	Petroleum (and natural gas) produced via wells from underground reservoirs formed in porous rock formations.
Dispatchable electricity supply	Electricity supply from generators that are demand-responsive i.e. for which output can be increased and decreased to balance demand.
Energy	Defined by engineers as *the capacity to do work and transfer heat*. In more general terms, energy is the capacity to effect physical transformations—moving and changing the shape of matter. Its unit of measurement is the joule (J).
Fossil fuels	Coal, crude oil and natural gas. Energy sources formed from organic matter deposited in the earth's crust over a period of millions of years, that has undergone physical transformations as a result of being subjected to high pressures and temperatures.
Hydraulic fracturing	Technique for recovery of oil from low-permeability petroleum-bearing geological formations, also known as 'fracking'.
Hydrocarbons	Chemical compounds consisting primarily of hydrogen and carbon. The basic constituent of petroleum and natural gas.
Joule	Unit of energy in the International System.
Natural gas	Gas comprised of methane, the lightest hydrocarbon compound. It may also contain small quantities of ethane and propane, plus inert components such as carbon dioxide and nitrogen.
Petroleum	The general term encompassing naturally occurring unprocessed crude oil and its refined products. In some usage, it is taken to encompass all hydrocarbons including natural gas. This is a matter of convention. In other usage it includes only hydrocarbons that are liquid at ambient atmospheric temperature and pressure.

Power	Rate of energy use, measured in units of watts (W). 1 $W = 1\ J/s$.
Power density	The rate of energy use per unit of spatial area, typically the horizontal land area occupied by energy conversion and supply systems. Measured in units of watts per square metre (W/m^2).
Renewable energy	Energy from sources that are not depleted on timescales relevant to human societies. The largest source by far is electromagnetic radiation from the sun, a significant portion of which is transferred to atmospheric air circulation (wind). Hence solar and wind energy are the largest potential sources of renewable energy exploitable by humans. Other notable sources are hydraulic energy from water flowing under gravity, wave energy (both also derived from solar energy conversions), tidal energy and geothermal energy.
Technically recoverable resource	Volume of petroleum that can be produced from a given formation using currently available exploration and production technology, without consideration to cost. This is distinct from *reserves*, the quantity that can be produced economically at current prices.
Tight oil	Also known as shale oil. Light crude oil produced via hydraulic fracturing from low-permeability petroleum-bearing geological formations.
Total final energy use	The aggregate energy from all fuels and electricity supplied to end-use sectors of the economy. It consists of TPES less all losses associated with energy conversion, transmission and distribution.
Total primary energy supply	The energy associated with all sources at the point of appropriation for human purposes from natural deposits or flows, aggregated by heating value. It includes the energy used by the energy supply sector of the economy, as well as energy provided to the rest of the economy.
Unconventional oil (and gas)	Petroleum (and natural gas) produced by methods other than the conventional well method. Includes deep water oil, tar sands and tight oil (shale oil).

Endnotes

1   See e.g. International Energy Agency, 2017a, 'World energy outlook 2017: Executive summary'. Available at: https://www.iea.org/Textbase/npsum/weo2017SUM.pdf (accessed 28 February 2018).

2   'BP statistical review of world energy 2017'. Available at: https://www.bp.com/content/dam/bp/en/corporate/pdf/energy-economics/statistical-review-2017/bp-statistical-review-of-world-energy-2017-full-report.pdf (accessed 28 February 2018).

3   For instance, see a recent article by Richard Heinberg discussing the relationship between fracking and the premature claims of peak oil's demise. 'New US record-level oil production! Peak oil theory disproven! Not.' Available at: http://www.resilience.org/stories/2018-03-06/new-u-s-record-level-oil-production-peak-oil-theory-disproven-not/ (accessed 1 March 2018).

4   NASA, 'Long-term warming trend continued in 2017: NASA, NOAA.' Available at: https://www.nasa.gov/press-release/long-term-warming-trend-continued-in-2017-nasa-noaa (accessed 28 February 2018).

5   We note in this regard that the term 'fossil fuels' is a catch-all label for coal, oil and natural gas, each in turn providing a convenient label for a wide range of materials sharing certain characteristics but differing markedly with respect to others. There is limited substitutability amongst these fossil energy sources. Infrastructures and institutions, plant and equipment, are configured to work with materials the composition of which must remain within appropriately defined limits. Even within the context of a human-managed overall reduction trajectory for fossil fuel combustion, geophysical supply constraints that affect the availability of particular grades of fuels can have severe economic impacts; these impacts can then feed back in turn, adversely affecting the scope for managed influence over the emission reduction trajectory. Consider for instance the role of petroleum-derived liquid fuels in transport systems, and the reliance on these by the economic networks with which renewable energy systems are deployed. What impacts might disruption to global physical and financial economic systems have on this deployment programme? Consider, too, the extent to which the global attention to decarbonising energy supply focuses on stationary energy, and electricity in particular—the portions of final energy supply that are perhaps *furthest* in time from being geo-physically constrained. Meanwhile, large-scale electrification of passenger transport, and production of synthetic transport fuels using electricity, is envisaged. How might the substitution of electricity for diesel and gasoline affect the dynamics of gas and thermal coal markets? And can it safely be assumed that the impacts of geo-physical constraint on *these* fuels will not have interactive affects with potential to destabilise economic systems?

We think it would be unwise to underestimate the political imperative of maintaining economic stability for rapidly scaling the global effort to decarbonise economies. Given the intricate inter-relationships between fossil fuels and contemporary economic systems, deliberately diverting attention away from fossil energy resource depletion questions at this point in time, while it may on the surface appear warranted, holds the potential for inflicting nasty surprises.

6   We use the terms 'complexity' and 'complexification' here strictly in the social scientific sense employed by Joseph Tainter. Such socio-political (and related) complexification arises as tasks carried out by a society involve increasing role differentiation and specialisation, with attendant coordination needs. See Tainter, J. 1988. *The collapse of complex societies.* Cambridge: Cambridge University Press.

7   Diamond, J. 1998. *Guns, germs, and steel: The fate of human societies.* London: Vintage.

8   In fact, growing populations may also have started putting pressure on the local ecosystems of hunter-gatherer societies, such that agriculture became the only means of supporting the growing population. We see here how socio-political complexification can be supported by an energy surplus—allowing a problem to be solved—just as a problem can require the search for an energy surplus in order to solve it. See Tainter, 1988, Note 6 above.

9   Alexander, S. 2014. 'Voluntary simplification as an alternative to collapse'. *Foresight* 16(6): 550–566.

10 Tainter, 1988, Note 6 above (arguing that complexity has diminishing marginal returns, and that civilisations in the past have collapsed when they could no longer meet the energy demands of their increasing socio-political complexity).

11 England's industrial revolution in fact commenced in the 18th century with the application of hydro power to industrial-scale mechanised textile production. The scope and scale of this revolution was constrained, however, until coal-fired steam engines supplanted flowing water as the power source. See Ashton, T. S. 1968. *The Industrial Revolution 1760–1830.* Oxford: Oxford University Press.

12 Heating value of a barrel of oil: 159 l x 40 MJ/l = 6.4 GJ/bbl; converted to work at efficiency of say 25 % = 1.6 GJ/bbl. Annual manual labour by a human of average fitness: 75 W x 3600 s/h x 8 h/day x 5 days/week x 48 weeks/y = 520 MJ/y [https://en.wikipedia.org/wiki/Human_power] (accessed 1 March 2018). One barrel of oil therefore enables work equivalent to approximately 3.0 years of human labour. Note here that we have included the conversion efficiency from the heating value of oil to mechanical work, which accounts for why our figure is lower than the figures sometimes cited by other commentators (e.g. 8.6 or 11 years per barrel).

13 This includes conventional petroleum plus the full range of other liquid hydrocarbons.

14 Australia: TPES 5.21 toe/capita in 2015 (TPES = total primary energy supply; toe = tonnes of oil equivalent; data from IEA Key World Energy Statistics 2017), or 6.9 kW per capita; assume 25% conversion efficiency fuel to work; final energy services 6.9 x 0.25 = 1.7 kW/capita; assume 75 W per 'energy slave', 1700/75 = 22.7 'energy

slaves' per capita; assuming 'energy slaves' work 8-hour shifts continuously, 24/8 x
22.7 = 68 'energy slaves' in total. Germany: 3.77 toe/capita in 2015; USA: 6.80 toe/
capita in 2015; 'energy slave' range is 3.77/5.21 x 68 = 49 to 6.80/5.21 x 68 = 89.

15 'Agriculture in the United States'. Available at: https://en.wikipedia.org/wiki/
Agriculture_in_the_United_States (accessed 28 February 2018).

16 While oil is our focus, we acknowledge that the relationship between oil, gas and
coal use, as availability of each relative to the others changes, will be complex.
Some substitution between fossil fuels is possible and hence constraints on
the availability of one may be offset by increased exploitation of another. The
substitution of natural gas (including shale and coal seam gas) for coal in electricity
generation provides an illustrative case in point. Natural gas is favoured over coal
for its reduced climate impact (if fugitive gas emissions are sufficiently low), and so
with strong action on climate change we would expect to see a reduced demand
for coal and increased demand for gas. Natural gas is also the main feedstock for
the production of hydrogen though, and so the emergence of hydrogen as a major
transport fuel as a climate change response would see the electricity and transport
sectors increasingly competing for a common energy source. Furthermore, coal
can also be used as a feedstock for the production of liquid transport fuels, and
for production of hydrogen as a transport fuel. This has particular implications for
thinking about the relationship between oil depletion and climate change. If oil
depletion drives a shift to alternative transport fuels derived from coal and gas, in
preference to the widely anticipated shift to electrification of transport, then there
is potential for increased climate impacts from transport (though in principle this
could be countered by carbon capture and storage at the fuel production stage).
The depletion rate of oil resources, in conjunction with the global climate response
agenda, can therefore be expected to have complex influences on the depletion
rates for coal and gas—and vice versa for each.

17 Miller, R. & Sorrel, S. 2014. 'The future of oil supply'. *Phil. Trans. of the Royal
Society.* A372, 20130179: 6.

18 See e.g. Thompson, H. 2017. *Oil and the Western economic crisis.* London: Palgrave
Macmillan.

19 Hamilton, J. 2011. 'Historical oil shocks'. Available at: http://econweb.ucsd.
edu/~jhamilton/oil_history.pdf (accessed 1 March 2018).

20 Hamilton, J. 2012. 'Oil prices, exhaustible resources, and economic growth'.
(NBER working paper 17759)). Available at: http://www.nber.org/papers/w17759.
pdf (accessed 1 March 2018).

21 Tverberg, G. 2012. 'Oil supply limits and the continuing financial crisis'. *Energy*
37(1): 27–34.

22 Ayres, R. 2014. *The bubble economy: Is sustainable growth possible?* Cambridge:
MIT Press.

23 See e.g. Ahmed, N. 2017. *Failing states, collapsing systems: Biophysical triggers of
political violence.* New York: Springer.

24 Fustier, K., Gray, G., Gundersen, C. & Hilboldt, T. 2016. 'Global oil supply: Will mature field declines drive the next supply crunch?' HSBC Global Research Report (September 2016). Available at: https://drive.google.com/file/d/oB9wSgViWVAfzUEgzMlBfR3UxNDg/view (accessed 1 March 2018); International Energy Agency, 2017a, see Note 1 above.

25 Mushalik, M. 2016. 'World outside US and Canada doesn't produce more crude oil than in 2005'. Crude oil peak. Available at: http://crudeoilpeak.info/world-outside-us-and-canada-doesnt-produce-more-crude-oil-than-in-2005 (accessed 1 March 2018).

26 Hirsch, R. 2007. 'Peaking of world oil production: Recent forecasts' (DOE/NETL-20017/1263): 13. Available at: https://netl.doe.gov/File%20Library/Research/Energy%20Analysis/Publications/DOE-NETL-2007-1263-PeakingWorldOilProd-RecentForecasts.pdf (accessed 1 March 2018).

27 Fustier et al., 2016, Note 24 above: 1.

28 Cunningham, N. 2017. 'Oil major: 70% of crude can be left in the ground'. Available at: https://oilprice.com/Energy/Crude-Oil/Oil-Major-70-Of-Crude-Can-Be-Left-In-The-Ground.html (accessed 1 March 2018).

29 EIA, 2017. 'Tight oil expected to make up most of US oil production increase through 2040'. Available at: https://www.eia.gov/todayinenergy/detail.php?id=29932; and International Energy Agency. 2017a. 'World Energy Outlook 2017'. Available at: https://www.iea.org/weo2017/ (accessed 1 March 2018).

30 See Note 24 above. See also, Rapier, R. 2017. 'Peak oil demand is millions of barrels away'. Available at: https://www.forbes.com/sites/rrapier/2017/06/19/peak-oil-demand-is-millions-of-barrels-away/#38c0a10f6940 (accessed 1 March 2018).

31 Hughes, D. 2018. 'Shale reality check: Drilling into the U.S. government's rosy projections for shale and gas oil production through 2050.' Post Carbon Institute Report (4 February 2018). Available at: https://www.postcarbon.org/publications/shale-reality-check/# (accessed 20 August 2018).

32 DiChristopher, T. 2017. 'Global crude oil discoveries plunge to record low, and it's gonna get worse'. Available at: https://www.cnbc.com/2017/04/27/global-crude-oil-discoveries-plunge-to-record-low-and-its-gonna-get-worse.html (accessed 1 March 2018).

33 Paraskova, T. 2017. 'US shale's most productive play may peak by 2021'. Available at: https://oilprice.com/Energy/Crude-Oil/US-Shales-Most-Productive-Play-May-Peak-By-2021.html (accessed 1 March 2018).

34 Patterson, R. 2017. 'US shale could peak before 2025'. Available at: https://oilprice.com/Energy/Energy-General/US-Shale-Could-Peak-Before-2025.html (accessed 1 March 2018); and Stafford, J. 2017. 'The IEA is grossly overestimating shale growth'. Available at: https://oilprice.com/Energy/Oil-Prices/The-IEA-Is-Grossly-Overestimating-Shale-Growth.html (accessed 1 March 2018).

35 Montgomery, J. B. & O'Sullivan, F. M. 2017. 'Spatial variability of tight oil well productivity and the impact of technology'. *Applied Energy* 195: 344–355.

36 Polson, J. & Loh, T. 2017. 'US vastly overestimates oil output forecasts, MIT study suggests'. Available at: https://www.bloomberg.com/news/articles/2017-12-01/mit-study-suggests-u-s-vastly-overstates-oil-output-forecasts (accessed 1 March 2018).

37 See e.g. Olson, B. & Cook, L. 2017. 'Wall Street tells frackers to stop counting barrels, start making profits'. Available at: https://www.wsj.com/articles/wall-streets-fracking-frenzy-runs-dry-as-profits-fail-to-materialize-1512577420 (accessed 1 March 2018); Davey, B. 2016. 'Shale euphoria: The boom and bust of sub prime oil and natural gas.' Available at: http://www.resilience.org/stories/2016-03-24/shale-euphoria-the-boom-and-bust-of-sub-prime-oil-and-natural-gas/ (accessed 1 March 2018).

38 Calcuttawala, Z. 2017. 'Higher oil prices reduce North American oil bankruptcies'. Available at: https://oilprice.com/Latest-Energy-News/World-News/Higher-Oil-Prices-Reduce-North-American-Oil-Bankruptcies.html (accessed 1 March 2018).

39 See e.g. Olson, B. & Cook, L. 2017. 'US shale juggernaut shows sign of fatigue'. Available at: https://www.wsj.com/articles/u-s-shale-juggernaut-shows-signs-of-fatigue-1507195802 (accessed 1 March 2018).

40 Note, though, that the analysis on which the Hirsch Report is based does not build in significant energy conservation measures, focusing almost entirely on supply-side responses. The report does include a section titled 'Conservation', but this focuses exclusively on end-use efficiency improvements via technology change, rather than societal-level re-evaluation of the uses or the purposes to which liquid fuels are directed. There is also one mention of 'structural conservation', as a possible wildcard that could ease the effects of peaking oil production, but this is envisaged only after a decade or more of high oil prices. A supply-side-only response is entirely inadequate, as we argue in this book. Had Hirsch taken into account more comprehensive demand-side response measures, it seems reasonable to expect that his timeline and costing would both reduce very significantly.

41 Hirsch, R. 2012. 'Peak Oil: Some knowns and unknowns'. ASPOUSA presentation (December 2012). Available at: https://www.youtube.com/watch?v=PVoDYha8ZRM (accessed 20 August 2018). See especially comments at 5 minutes.

42 Cunningham, N. 2016. 'Oil price spike inevitable as new discoveries hit seventy year low' Oil Price (30 August, 2016). Available at: https://oilprice.com/Energy/Crude-Oil/Oil-Price-Spike-Inevitable-As-New-Discoveries-Hit-Seventy-Year-Low.html (accessed 20 August 2018); and International Energy Agency, 2016. 'Global oil discoveries and new projects fell to historic lows in 2016'. Available at: https://www.iea.org/newsroom/news/2017/april/global-oil-discoveries-and-new-projects-fell-to-historic-lows-in-2016.html (accessed 1 March 2018).

43 Oyedele, A. 2017. 'Oil discoveries are at an all-time low—and the clock is ticking'. Available at: http://www.businessinsider.com/oil-discoveries-fall-to-lowest-since-1940s-2017-12/?r=AU&IR=T (accessed 1 March 2018).

44 International Energy Agency, 2016, see Note 42 above.

45 Fustier et al., 2016, Note 24 above: 4.

46 On oil's EROI, see Murphy, D. 2014. 'The implications of the declining energy return on investment of oil production'. *Phil. Trans. of the Royal Society A.* 372(2006). Available at: http://rsta.royalsocietypublishing.org/content/372/2006/20130126 (accessed 1 March 2018).

47 Murphy, 2014, see Note 46 above.

48 See, for instance, Dale, M., Krumdieck, S. & Bodger, P. 2011. 'Net energy yield from production of conventional oiloil'. *Energy Policy*, 39(11),): 7095–7102. doi: https://doi.org/10.1016/j.enpol.2011.08.021

49 Scheyder, E. & McWilliams, G. 2017. 'Oil majors still years from repairing balance sheets after price war'. Available at: https://www.reuters.com/article/us-ceraweek-spending/oil-majors-still-years-from-repairing-balance-sheets-after-price-war-idUSKBN16F27F (accessed 1 March 2018).

50 Heinberg, R. & Fridley, D. 2015. *Our renewable future: Laying the path for one hundred percent clean energy*. Washington: Island Press. Available at: http://ourrenewablefuture.org/#the-book (accessed 1 March 2018).

51 Angelo, S. 2017. 'World's largest oil companies: Deep trouble as profits vaporize while debts skyrocket'. Available at: https://srsroccoreport.com/worlds-largest-oil-companies-deep-trouble-as-profits-vaporize-while-debts-skyrocket/ (accessed 1 March 2018).

52 Kopits, S. 2014. 'Oil and economic growth: A supply-constrained view' (11 February 2014). Available at: http://energypolicy.columbia.edu/sites/default/files/Kopits%20-%20Oil%20and%20Economic%20Growth%20(SIPA,%202014)%20-%20Presentation%20Version%5B1%5D.pdf (accessed 1 March 2018).

53 Angelo, 2017, see Note 51 above.

54 Foeger, L. 2017. 'Oil price collapse cost OPEC countries over $1tn'. Available at: https://www.rt.com/business/406820-opec-oil-prices-collapse-losses/ (accessed 1 March 2018).

55 Adams, C. 2014. 'Oil price threatens $1tn of projects'. *Financial Times* (14 December). Available at: https://www.ft.com/content/b3d67518-845f-11e4-bae9-00144feabdc0 (accessed 1 March 2018).

56 Gosden, E. 2016. 'Oil demand peak "not in sight" as stage set for boom and bust, says IEA'. Available at: http://www.telegraph.co.uk/business/2016/11/16/oil-demand-peak-not-in-sight-as-stage-set-for-boom-and-bust-says/ (accessed 1 March 2018).

57 Gosden, E. 2016. 'Oil supply crunch "to hit in 2019" as investment in new projects dries up'. Available at: http://www.telegraph.co.uk/business/2016/11/22/oil-supply-crunch-hit-2019-investment-new-projects-dries/ (accessed 1 March 2018).

58 Cho, S. & Cheong, S. 2017. 'Citi says get ready for an oil squeeze'. Available at: https://www.bloomberg.com/news/articles/2017-09-25/citi-says-get-ready-for-an-oil-squeeze-than-an-opec-supply-surge (accessed 1 March 2018); Schaps, K. and Dolan, D. 2017. 'Aramco CEO sees oil supply shortage as investments, discoveries drop'. Available at: https://www.reuters.com/article/us-aramco-oil/aramco-ceo-sees-oil-supply-shortage-as-investments-discoveries-drop-idUSKBN19V0KR (accessed 1 March 2018); and Helal, Y. 2016. 'More spending cuts as UAE predicts oil shortages'. Available at: http://www.arabianindustry.com/oil-gas/news/2016/nov/6/more-spending-cuts-as-uae-predicts-oil-shortages-5531344/ (accessed 1 March 2018).

59 This situation also has implications for political stability, as a peak in oil exports also means (in the absence of significant oil price increase) a peak in oil *revenue* for the exporting nation. The situation that arises when nations significantly dependent on oil export revenue encounter the consequences of increasing domestic demand and stagnating production has been termed the Export Land Effect, after the Export Land Model developed by Brown and Foucher. See Brown, J. and Foucher, S. 2008. 'A quantitative assessment of future net oil exports by the top five net oil exporters'. *Energy Bulletin*. January 8. http://www.resilience.org/stories/2008-01-08/quantitative-assessment-future-net-oil-exports-top-five-net-oil-exporters/ (accessed 1 March 2018). For discussion of the political implications of the Export Land Effect, see Ahmed, 2016, Note 23 above.

60 Patterson, R. 2014. 'World crude oil exports'. Available at: http://peakoilbarrel.com/world-crude-oil-exports/ (accessed 1 March 2018).

61 Neslen, A. 2016. 'Europe's oil imports "dependent on unstable countries"'. Available at: https://www.theguardian.com/environment/2016/jul/12/europes-oil-imports-dependent-on-unstable-countries (accessed 1 March 2018).

62 See Note 59 above. See also e.g. Fahey, M. 2015. 'Oil prices and budgets: The OPEC countries most at risk'. Available at: https://www.cnbc.com/2015/12/03/oil-prices-and-budgetsthe-opec-countries-most-at-risk.html (accessed 1 March 2018).

63 Husain, A. et al. 2015. 'Global implications of lower oil prices' (SDN/15/15). Available at: https://www.imf.org/external/pubs/ft/sdn/2015/sdn1515.pdf (accessed 1 March 2018).

64 Shahine, A. & Khraiche, D. 2017. 'Oil cuts add to Saudi pain as GDP contracts for second quarter'. Available at: https://www.bloomberg.com/news/articles/2017-09-30/saudi-gdp-shrinks-for-second-quarter-in-a-row-amid-opec-cuts (accessed 1 March 2018).

65 Biello, D. 2013. 'How much will tar sands oil add to global warming?'. Scientific American (23 January 2013). Available at: https://www.scientificamerican.com/article/tar-sands-and-keystone-xl-pipeline-impact-on-global-warming/ (accessed 1 March 2018); Kharecha, P. & Hansen, J. 2008. 'Implications of "peak oil" for atmospheric CO_2 and climate'. Available at: https://arxiv.org/ftp/arxiv/papers/0704/0704.2782.pdf (accessed 1 March 2018).

66 McGlade, C. & Ekins, P. 2015. 'The geographical distribution of fossil fuels unused when limiting global warming to 2 degrees'. *Nature* 517: 187–190. Available at: https://www.nature.com/articles/nature14016 (accessed 1 March 2018).

67 For these types of reasons we argue that there is no 'optimal' price for oil in much the same way as there is no 'optimal' price for heroin. At first this analogy may appear like a polemical exaggeration, but in fact it is worryingly apt. When heroin is expensive, users cannot afford what they desperately want, and suffer accordingly. Expenditure on other needs is cut back in order to fund the increasingly expensive and debilitating addiction. But when heroin is cheap and readily available, the negative consequences of addiction are exacerbated through greater consumption, and the ill effects only deepen as the prospect of breaking free of addiction's grip recedes. Oil acts as industrial civilisation's own form of heroin, and, whether it is cheap or expensive, addicts today are in as much trouble as ever.

68 Murphy, D. & Hall, C. 2011. Energy return on investment, peak oil, and the end of economic growth. *Annals of the New York Academy of Sciences*, 1219(1), 52–72. doi: 10.1111/j.1749-6632.2010.05940.x: 52.

69 Murphy, T. 2011. 'The energy trap'. *Do the Math*. (18 October). Available at: https://dothemath.ucsd.edu/2011/10/the-energy-trap/ (accessed 4 October 2018).

70 Mohr, S. et al. 2015. 'Projection of world fossil fuels by country'. *Fuel* 141: 120–35.

71 See for instance the this recent article on implications of methane release from melting permafrost: Comyn-Platt, E. et al. 2018. 'Carbon budgets for 1.5 and 2 °C targets lowered by natural wetland and permafrost feedbacks'. *Nature Geoscience*, 11(8), 568-573. doi: 10.1038/s41561-018-0174-9.

72 Hausfather, Z. 2018. 'How much "carbon budget" is left to limit global warming to 1.5C?' *Ecologise.in*. (18 April). Available at: https://www.ecologise. in/2018/04/18/how-much-carbon-budget-is-left-to-limit-global-warming-to-1-5c/ (accessed 2 July 2018).

73 For arguments generally along these lines, see: Peters, G. P. 2018. Beyond carbon budgets. *Nature Geoscience*, 11(6): 378–380. doi: 10.1038/s41561-018-0142-4; and Geden, O. 2018. 'Politically informed advice for climate action'. *Nature Geoscience*. doi: 10.1038/s41561-018-0143-3.

74 'The Paris Agreement'. 2015. Available at: https://unfccc.int/files/meetings/paris_ nov_2015/application/pdf/paris_agreement_english_.pdf (accessed 1 March 2018).

75 King, A., Karoly, D. & Henley, B. 2017. 'Australian climate extremes at 1.5C and 2C of global warming', *Nature Climate Change* 7:412-416.

76 Comyn-Platt, E. et al. 2018, see Note 71 above.

77 See e.g. Jordan, A. et al. 2013. 'Going beyond two degrees? The risks and opportunities of alternative options'. *Climate Policy* 13(6): 751–769. See also Spratt, D. 2017 'Paris 1.5-2C target far from safe, say world-leading scientists'. Available at: http://reneweconomy.com.au/paris-1-5-2c-target-far-from-safe-say-world-leading-scientists-81532/ (accessed 1 March 2018).

78 As researchers note: 'there are no scenarios that have a high probability of limiting warming below the 1.5°C limit during the entire 21st century.' Rogelj, L. et al. 2015. 'Energy system transformations for limiting end-of-century warming to below 1.5C'. *Nature Climate Change* 5: 519–526. See also, Carbon Tracker Initiative & Grantham Research Institute. 2013. 'Unburnable carbon 2013: Wasted capital and stranded assets'. Available at: http://carbontracker.live.kiln.digital/ Unburnable-Carbon-2-Web-Version.pdf (accessed 1 March 2018).

79 Spratt, D. & Dunlop, I. 2017. 'What lies beneath: The scientific understatement of climate risks'. Breakthrough Institute: 15. Available at: https://docs.wixstatic. com/ugd/148cb0_56b252a7d78b485badde2fadcba88d00.pdf (accessed 1 March 2018). See also, Spratt, D. 2016. 'Unravelling the myth of a "carbon budget" for 1.5C'. Available at: http://www.climatecodered.org/2016/09/unravelling-myth-of-carbon-budget-for.html (accessed 1 March 2018).

80 Anderson, K. 2015a. 'Duality in climate science'. *Nature Geoscience* 8: 898–900.

81 Spratt, D. 2016. 'Unravelling the myth of a "carbon budget" for 1.5C', Note 79 above.

82 Campbell, K. et al. 2007. 'The age of consequences: The foreign policy and national security implications of global climate change'. *Centre for Strategic and International Studies & Centre for New American Security*, Washington.

83 Spratt, 2016, see Note 79 above.

84 Spratt, D. 2014. 'The real budgetary emergency and the myth of "burnable carbon"'. *Climate Code Red* (22 May). Available at: http://www.climatecodered.org/2014/05/ the-real-budgetary-emergency-burnable.html (accessed 1 March 2018).

85 Anderson, K. & Peters, G. 2016. 'The trouble with negative emissions'. *Science* 354(6309). Available at: http://smartstones.nl/wp-content/uploads/2016/12/ Kevin-Anderson-2016.10.13-the-Trouble-with-Negative-Emissions-Science-2016.pdf (accessed 1 March 2018).

86 Vaughan, N. & Gough, C. 2016. 'Expert assessment concludes negative emissions scenarios may not deliver'. *Environmental Research Letters*, 11(9), 095003. doi: doi:10.1088/1748-9326/11/9/095003.

87 Anderson, K. 2015b. 'Talks in the city of light generate more heat'. *Nature* 528: 437.

88 Rabinowitz, A. 2017. 'The dirty secret of the world's plan to avert climte disaster'. Available at: https://www.wired.com/story/the-dirty-secret-of-the-worlds-plan-to-avert-climate-disaster/ (accessed 1 March 2018).

89 Peters, G. & Geden, O. 2017. 'Catalysing a political shift from low to negative carbon'. *Nature Climate Change* 7: 619–621. Available at: https://www.nature. com/articles/nclimate3369 (accessed 1 March 2018).

90 Anderson & Peters, 2016, see Note 85 above.

91 Daley, J. 2017. 'Major "clean coal" project in Mississippi shuts down'. Available at: https://www.smithsonianmag.com/smart-news/major-clean-coal-project-mississippi-shut-down-180963898/ (accessed 1 March 2018).

92 Hamilton, C. 2014. *Earthmasters: The dawn of the age of climate engineering*. New Haven: Yale University Press.

93 See e.g. Ekanayake, P. K. B., Moriarty, J. P., and Honnery, D. R. 2015. 'Equity and energy in global solutions to climate change'. *Energy for Sustainable Development* 26: 72–78; and also Carzorla, M. & Toman, M. 2000. 'International Equity and Climate Change Policy' (Resources of the Future, Climate Issue Brief, No. 27).

94 Stern, N. 2007. 'Stern Review: The economics of climate change'. Available at: http://mudancasclimaticas.cptec.inpe.br/~rmclima/pdfs/destaques/sternreview_report_complete.pdf (accessed 1 March 2018).

95 Anderson, K. 2013. 'Avoiding climate change demands de-growth strategies'. Available at: https://kevinanderson.info/blog/avoiding-dangerous-climate-change-demands-de-growth-strategies-from-wealthier-nations/ (accessed 1 March 2018).

96 The question of appropriate climate action within poorer nations is an equally important issue but one that is not the focus of this analysis.

97 This critique often neglects the fact that, as evidenced by historical and archaeological records, economic growth is an inherent characteristic of all large-scale human societies. This is not a recent phenomenon, nor is it restricted to societies dominated by market economies, where the means of production are organised by market capitalism. Everywhere that institutional and technological developments have led to increases in the productivity of labour, the extra output has resulted in growth of the overall economy. David Fleming makes the case that growth inevitably follows productivity increase, because the additional output goes to building and maintaining the intermediate economy, or what he describes as the 'regrettable necessities which are required to support a large-scale civil society' (Fleming, D. 2016. *Lean Logic*. White River Junction: Chelsea Green Publishing: 185). As a large-scale society develops, the support systems that it requires in order to function grow at an increased rate relative to the size of the society as a whole: 'the larger the system, the larger the proportion of its total energy and output needed to build, and then maintain, its own complicated infrastructures...in terms of that ratio between the size of the support system and the size of the society, intensification is a process of increasing inefficiency' (p. 185). Tainter highlights a related phenomenon: large-scale societies generate their own problems; solving these problems entails increased socio-political complexity (differentiation and coordination of social roles); this entails increased resource use, especially energy resources (Tainter, 1988, Note 6 above).

98 Hiltzik, M. 2017. 'A Stanford professor didn't just debate his scientific critics—he sued them for $10 million'. Available at: http://www.latimes.com/business/hiltzik/la-fi-hiltzik-jacobson-lawsuit-20171121-story.html (accessed 1 March 2018).

99 A dispatchable electricity source is any source that can be brought on-line when required, without availability being subject to uncontrollable variability of the primary energy source, as is the case with wind and solar radiation.

100 Pearce, J. M. (2008). 'Thermodynamic limitations to nuclear energy deployment as a greenhouse gas mitigation technologytechnology'. *Int. J. of Nuclear Governance, Economy and Ecology*, 2(1),): 113–130. doi: 10.1504/IJNGEE.2008.017358.

101 Locatelli, G., Mancini, M. & Todeschini, N. 2013. 'Generation IV nuclear reactors: Current status and future prospects'. *Energy Policy*, 61: 1503–1520. doi: https://doi.org/10.1016/j.enpol.2013.06.101 (accessed 1 March 2018); Zhang, Z. et al. 2016. 'The Shandong Shidao Bay 200 MWe High-Temperature Gas-Cooled Reactor Pebble-Bed high-temperature gas-cooled reactor pebble-bed module (HTR-PM) Demonstration Power demonstration power plant: An engineering and Technological technological innovation'. *Engineering*, 2(1),): 112–118. doi: https://doi.org/10.1016/J.ENG.2016.01.020.

102 Castelvecchi, D. & Tollefson, J. 2016. 'US advised to stick with troubled fusion reactor ITER'. *Nature*, 27 May. Available at: https://www.nature.com/news/us-advised-to-stick-with-troubled-fusion-reactor-iter-1.19994 (accessed 19 June 2018).

103 The critical literature is extensive. For example, Clack, et al. 2017. 'Evaluation of a proposal for reliable low-cost grid power with 100% wind, water, and solar'. *PNAS* 114(26): 6722–6727; Moriarty, P. & Honnery, D. 2016. 'Can renewable energy power the future?' *Energy Policy* 93: 3–7; Smil, V. 2015. *Power density: Key to understanding energy sources and uses*. Cambridge: MIT Press; Castro, C. et al. 2013. 'Global solar electric potential: A review of their technical and sustainable limits'. *Renewable and Sustainable Energy Reviews* 28: 824–835; Hirth, L. 2013. 'The market value of variable renewables: The effect of solar and wind power variability on their relative price'. *Energy Economics* 38: 218–236; Moriarty, P. & Honnery, D. 2011. Rise and Fall of the Carbon Civilisation. London: Springer.

104 The theoretical potential for renewable energy is the total energy flowing through the earth system. So for instance in relation to solar energy (by several orders of magnitude the largest source, and also the primary source for wind energy, as this drives the global atmospheric circulation), the theoretical potential is the electromagnetic radiation from the sun that arrives on the earth's surface. It is even higher, if we can conceive of intercepting the sun's radiation beyond the earth's atmosphere. This can be thought of as the 'pool' from which energy flows for human use can be extracted, but it does not represent an upper limit for human exploitation. This limit is likely to be orders of magnitude smaller.

105 See generally, Moriarty, P. & Honnery, D. 2012. 'Preparing for a low-energy future'. *Futures* 44(10): 883–892.

106 Current demand patterns have been established in the context of incumbent supply systems, and so are subject to modification as supply context shifts and appropriate incentives are available. As such, the demand patterns familiar today are not written in stone, and a shift to renewable energy almost certainly implies a shift to more flexible grids, where demand patterns must change to accommodate supply characteristics. This has far-ranging consequences, though, for social and economic systems, and these have considerable inertia that will limit the extent and rate of change that can be realised. Nonetheless, this is an area where technology and market changes can and almost certainly will have a significant impact.

107 The electricity sources that have historically been used to provide base-load power also meet the requirements for dispatchability, as they can be scheduled to come on-line at an agreed time in the future. Typically, these sources are

unable to adjust output fast enough to respond to the short-term fluctuations in demand that characterise normal grid operation. To accommodate these more rapid changes, dispatchable sources with what is known as 'load-following' capability are also required. Historically this capability has mainly been provided by hydroelectric, gas turbine and diesel generators.

108 While in principle this strategy appears attractive, it is not yet clear that it can provide sufficient reliability, even if cost were no barrier to grid expansion. There have been numerous events in recent years where the entire Euro region has been becalmed. See, e.g. Mearns, E. 2015. 'The wind in Spain blows.' *Energy Matters* (30 November). Available at: http://euanmearns.com/the-wind-in-spain-blows/ (accessed 20 August 2018) (reviewing data and concluding that, 'On a regular basis the whole of Europe is becalmed'). Similar events have been noted in Australia and elsewhere. See McArdle, P. 2018. Various articles tagged 'wind diversity'. *Watt Clarity*. Available at: http://www.wattclarity.com.au/tag/wind-diversity/ (accessed 20 August 2018).

109 A recent national electricity grid study finds that the multiple is in the order of 3 to 4 times. See Lenzen, M., McBain, B., Trainer, T., Jütte, S., Rey-Lescure, O. & Huang, J. 2016. 'Simulating low-carbon electricity supply for Australia'. *Applied Energy* 179: 553–564. doi: http://dx.doi.org/10.1016/j.apenergy.2016.06.151 (accessed 1 March 2018).

110 See for instance, Trainer, T. 2017. 'Some problems in storing renewable energy'. *Energy Policy*, 110 (Supplement C): 386–393. doi: https://doi.org/10.1016/j.enpol.2017.07.061 (accessed 1 March 2018). This perspective relates specifically to the Australian context, rather than the global situation, but Australia's energy use provides a sufficiently close analogue to the global pattern that the findings are broadly relevant to our case here.

111 International Energy Agency, 2017b. No title. Presentation at launch event for the World Energy Outlook 2017. Available at: https://www.facebook.com/internationalenergyagency/videos/10157417220717228/ (accessed 20 August 2018).

112 Friedmann, A. 2016. *When the trucks stop running: Energy and the future of transportation*. New York: Springer. There are precedents for running mining operations on electricity. For example, when South Africa's apartheid regime faced economic sanctions in the 1980s that blocked the country's oil supply, a response was to convert mining equipment to electrical power using overhead catenary wires. Nonetheless, doing this as comprehensively and on the scale that a global or even national transition to 100% renewably generated electricity would require would present significantly larger challenges than those faced by South Africa.

113 See, for instance, Krumdieck, S. & Page, S. 2013. 'Retro-analysis of liquid bio-ethanol and bio-diesel in New Zealand'. *Energy Policy*, 62: 363–371. doi: https://doi.org/10.1016/j.enpol.2013.07.078.

114 Palmer, G. 2014. *Energy in Australia: Peak oil, solar power, and Asia's economic growth*. New York: Springer.

115 Jacobson, M. et al. 2017. '100% clean and renewable wind, water, and sunlight all-sector energy roadmaps for 139 countries of the world'. *Joule* 1: 108–121.

116 Palmer, G. & Floyd, J. 2017. 'An exploration of divergence in EPBT and EROI for solar photovoltaics'. *BioPhysical Economics and Resource Quality* 2(4): 1–20. doi: 10.1007/s41247-017-0033-0.

117 Ayres, R. & Voudouris, V. 2014. 'The economic growth enigma: Capital, labour and useful energy'. *Energy Policy* 64(C): 16–26; Kalimeris, P., Richardson, C. & Bithas, K. 2014. 'A meta-analysis investigation of the direction of the energy-GDP causal relationship: Implications for the growth-degrowth dialogue'. *Journal of Cleaner Production* 67: 1–13.

118 Smil, V. 2015, see Note 103 above.

119 Smil, V. 2010. *Energy transitions: History, requirements, and prospects.* Santa Barbara: Prager Publishers.

120 An important question arises here with respect to the political implications of the transition. The transition is likely to be self-supporting if its benefits are personal and experienced as significant at the individual or household level. If the benefits are personal and insignificant at that level, incentives are needed. If the benefits accrue collectively at the national level, then even if experienced as significant at that level, regulation by national governments is needed. If the benefits are international and significant, global agreement is needed. But if the benefits are international, and experienced as insignificant in the short term relative to incumbent arrangements, it is difficult to see how the transition will occur.

121 Van den Bergh, J., Folke, C., Polasky, S., Scheffer, M. & Steffan, W. 2015. 'What if solar energy becomes really cheap? A thought experiment on environmental problem shifting'. *Environmental Sustainability* 14: 170–179. doi: https://doi.org/10.1016/j.cosust.2015.05.007.

122 See generally, Alexander, S. 2015. *Prosperous descent: Crisis as opportunity in an age of limits.* Melbourne, Simplicity Institute; Floyd, J. 2014. 'Sense-making and acting for descent futures: Human and cultural pathways'. *Foresight* 16(6): 586–607; Trainer, T. 2010. *The transition to a sustainable and just world.* Sydney: Envirobook; Holmgren, D. 2009. *Future scenarios: Mapping the cultural implications of peak oil and climate change.* Available at: http://www.futurescenarios.org/ (accessed 1 March 2018); Fleming, D. 2016. *Lean logic: a dictionary for the future and how to survive it.* White River Junction: Chelsea Green.

123 As noted earlier, we use the terms 'complexity' and 'complexification' here strictly in the social scientific sense employed by Tainter, 1988, Note 6 above. Such socio-political (and related) complexification arises as tasks carried out by a society involve increasing role differentiation and specialisation, with attendant coordination needs. Others argue, and we have much regard for this perspective also, that these characteristics of large-scale societies actually involve *simplification*, and that the outcome is better described as *complication* rather than *complexity*. See for instance the entry on Complexity in Fleming's (2016: 74–8) *Lean logic*, Note 122 above. The point here is that the structures and institutions employed by large-scale societies to enable their ongoing socio-political complexification and growth typically involve uniformity and standardisation—an ironing out of the local, context-responsive nuances and adaptations that give traditional societies their depth and richness of cultural integrity, that in turn has underpinned their long-

term viability (at least until confronted by modernity's power to force all before it into its monocultural template). This is the very opposite of what social and cultural complexity could typically be taken to mean, by participants in those traditional societies, in senses other than the narrow social scientific one that for expediency we adopt here. For instance, members of traditional societies often develop astonishingly nuanced sensory capacities and attendant linguistic and conceptual palettes responsive to their particular natural and social environmental situations. The world as it appears to such capacities is very often imperceptible, even unimaginable, to members of modern societies. Wade Davis's remarkable book *The Wayfinders: Why ancient wisdom matters in the modern world* (2009. Toronto: House of Anasasi Press) is essential reading here. For a quick introduction, see his TED talks available at https://www.ted.com/speakers/wade_davis (accessed 14 June 2018). For exploration of these ideas specifically in the context of descent, see Floyd, 2014, Note 122 above.

124 Tainter, 1988, see Note 6 above, discussing the diminishing returns on complexity.

125 Drawing on Sidney Pollard's characterisation of the progress idea, viewed as perhaps modernity's preeminent cultural narrative. See Pollard, S. 1968. *The idea of progress: History and society.* London: C.A. Watts.

126 Again though, we do not wish that the central points made here be obscured by arguments around terminology. As noted above, it can be persuasively argued that the characteristics of large-scale societies as they solve problems and grow are better described in terms of simplification rather that complexification. So the 'voluntary simplification' that we have in mind is really about moving the development of societies in a very different direction to that typical for large-scale societies. This has also been described as economic deintensification, based on promotion and support for developing informal economies at the community, neighbourhood and household scale. Once again, see Fleming's *Lean logic,* 2016, Note 122 above, for extensive discussion of what we are terming 'voluntary simplification', in terms of 'economic deintensification'.

127 Reduced *production activity* within the context of the incumbent socio-political-economic arrangements does not necessarily imply reduced *productive activity*. Indeed, the activity that continues in the wake of such a change process, supplanting the production activity of the incumbent political economy, may well be *more* productive, in the sense of producing more of what people actually desire in order to lead fulfilled lives, and doing so with less overall use of resources. Arrangements that fulfil ordinary citizens' desires for valuable goods and services while using fewer resources (and even regenerating the productive resource context) should surely be regarded as increasing rather than decreasing productivity. Measures, indicators and the metaphors on which they're built need to adapt also to the shifting context.

128 A strong argument can be made that the growth of informal economies would actually allow a return to focus on meeting people's *wants*, in preference to the *systemic needs* that are the predominant focus of industrial economies—where the majority of production activity goes towards supporting the means of production itself, rather than to actually providing the things that people want in their day-to-day lives. Yet again, see Fleming, 2016, Note 122 above.

129 See generally, Alexander, S. & McLeod, A. (eds). 2014. *Simple living in history: Pioneers of the deep future.* Melbourne: Simplicity Institute.

130 Alternatively, personal car use might continue, albeit on a smaller scale, but change radically based on shared access and task-appropriate choice amongst a range of viable alternatives. A growing role for lightweight battery electric vehicles, such as cargo bicycles, can also be readily envisaged.

131 On the question of local versus regional versus global supply chains, there is a case for treating this not as one-size-fits-all, but rather to view the question through a lens of *mindful production and consumption*, where the acceptable length of supply chains depends on the nature of the goods or services in question. There may well be justification for long supply chains for very high value goods in much smaller quantities, due to relative advantages in production and differences in need. And then again, there may be entirely different ways available to us for engaging with such questions. Consider how adopting the 'chain' metaphor itself influences sense-making in relation to the means by which wants are met. How might this be affected by adopting the metaphor of, say, a 'web' in place of a 'chain'?

132 Bateson, N. 2017. *Small arcs of larger circles: Framing through other patterns.* 2nd ed. Axminster: Triarchy Press.

133 Fleming, 2016, see Note 122 above.

134 Anderson, 2015, see Note 87 above.

135 Tainter, J. 2006. 'Social complexity and sustainability'. *Ecological Complexity* 3: 91–103: 99.

Bibliography

Adams, C. 2014. 'Oil price threatens $1tn of projects'. *Financial Times* (14 December). Available at: https://www.ft.com/content/b3d67518-845f-11e4-bae9-00144feabdc0 (accessed 1 March 2018).

Ahmed, N. 2017. *Failing states, collapsing systems: Biophysical triggers of political violence*. New York: Springer.

Alexander, S. 2014. 'Voluntary simplification as an alternative to collapse'. *Foresight* 16(6): 550–566.

Alexander, S. 2015. *Prosperous descent: Crisis as opportunity in an age of limits*. Melbourne, Simplicity Institute.

Alexander, S. & McLeod, A. (eds). 2014. *Simple living in history: Pioneers of the deep future*. Melbourne: Simplicity Institute.

Alexander, S., Rutherford, J. & Floyd, J. 2018. 'A critique of the Australian National Outlook decoupling strategy: A "Limits to Growth" perspective.' *Ecological Economics* 145: 10–17. doi: https://doi.org/10.1016/j.ecolecon.2017.08.014 (accessed 1 March 2018).

Allen, T. F. H., Tainter, J. A. & Hoekstra, T. W. 2003. *Supply-side sustainability*. New York: Columbia University Press.

Anderson, K. 2013. 'Avoiding climate change demands de-growth strategies'. Available at: https://kevinanderson.info/blog/avoiding-dangerous-climate-change-demands-de-growth-strategies-from-wealthier-nations/ (accessed 1 March 2018).

Anderson, K. 2015a. 'Duality in climate science'. *Nature Geoscience* 8: 898–900.

Anderson, K. 2015b. 'Talks in the city of light generate more heat'. *Nature* 528: 437.

Anderson, K. & Peters, G. 2016. 'The trouble with negative emissions'. *Science* 354(6309). Available at: http://smartstones.nl/wp-content/uploads/2016/12/Kevin-Anderson-2016.10.13-the-Trouble-with-Negative-Emissions-Science-2016.pdf (accessed 1 March 2018).

Angelo, S. 2017. 'World's largest oil companies: Deep trouble as profits vaporize while debts skyrocket'. Available at: https://srsroccoreport.com/worlds-largest-oil-companies-deep-trouble-as-profits-vaporize-while-debts-skyrocket/ (accessed 1 March 2018).

Ashton, T. S. 1968. *The Industrial Revolution 1760–1830*. Oxford: Oxford University Press.

Ayres, R. 2014. *The bubble economy: Is sustainable growth possible?* Cambridge: MIT Press.

Ayres, R. & Voudouris, V. 2014. 'The economic growth enigma: Capital, labour and useful energy'. *Energy Policy* 64(C): 16–26.

Bardi, U. 2013. *The Limits to Growth Revisited*. New York: Springer.

Bateson, N. 2017. *Small Arcs of Larger Circles: Framing Through Other Patterns*. 2nd ed. Axminster: Triarchy Press.

Biello, D. 2013. 'How much will tar sands oil add to global warming?'. *Scientific American* (23 January 2013). Available at: https://www.scientificamerican.com/article/tar-sands-and-keystone-xl-pipeline-impact-on-global-warming/ (accessed 1 March 2018).

'BP Statistical Review of World Energy 2017'. Available at: https://www.bp.com/content/dam/bp/en/corporate/pdf/energy-economics/statistical-review-2017/bp-statistical-review-of-world-energy-2017-full-report.pdf (accessed 28 February 2018).

Brown, J. & Foucher, S. 2008. 'A quantitative assessment of future net oil exports by the top five net oil exporters'. *Energy Bulletin*. January 8. http://www.resilience.org/stories/2008-01-08/quantitative-assessment-future-net-oil-exports-top-five-net-oil-exporters/ (accessed 1 March 2018).

Calcuttawala, Z. 2017. 'Higher oil prices reduce North American oil bankruptcies'. Available at: https://oilprice.com/Latest-Energy-News/World-News/Higher-Oil-Prices-Reduce-North-American-Oil-Bankruptcies.html (accessed 1 March 2018).

Campbell, K. et al. 2007. 'The age of consequences: The foreign policy and national security implications of global climate change'. *Centre for Strategic and International Studies & Centre for New American Security*, Washington.

Carbon Tracker Initiative & Grantham Research Institute. 2013. 'Unburnable carbon 2013: Wasted capital and stranded assets'. Available at: http://carbontracker.live.kiln.digital/Unburnable-Carbon-2-Web-Version.pdf (accessed 1 March 2018).

Carzorla, M. & Toman, M. 2000. 'International Equity and Climate Change Policy' (Resources of the Future, Climate Issue Brief, No. 27).

Castelvecchi, D. & Tollefson, J. 2016. 'US advised to stick with troubled fusion reactor ITER'. *Nature*, 27 May. Available at: https://www.nature.com/news/us-advised-to-stick-with-troubled-fusion-reactor-iter-1.19994 (accessed 19 June 2018).

Castro, C. et al. 2013. 'Global solar electric potential: A review of their technical and sustainable limits'. *Renewable and Sustainable Energy Reviews* 28: 824–835.

Checkland, P. B. & Poulter, J. 2006. *Learning for action: A short definitive account of Soft Systems Methodology, and its use for practitioners, teachers and students*. London: John Wiley & Sons.

Cho, S. and Cheong, S. 2017. 'Citi says get ready for an oil squeeze'. Available at: https://www.bloomberg.com/news/articles/2017-09-25/citi-says-get-ready-for-an-oil-squeeze-than-an-opec-supply-surge (accessed 1 March 2018).

Clack, C. et al. 2017. 'Evaluation of a proposal for reliable low-cost grid power with 100% wind, water, and solar'. *PNAS* 114(26): 6722–6727.

Comyn-Platt, E. et al. 2018. 'Carbon budgets for 1.5 and 2 °C targets lowered by natural wetland and permafrost feedbacks'. *Nature Geoscience*, 11(8), 568-573. doi: 10.1038/s41561-018-0174-9.

Cunningham, N. 2016. 'Oil price spike inevitable as new discoveries hit seventy year low' *Oil Price* (30 August, 2016). Available at: https://oilprice.com/Energy/Crude-Oil/Oil-Price-Spike-Inevitable-As-New-Discoveries-Hit-Seventy-Year-Low.html (accessed 20 August 2018).

Cunningham, N. 2017. 'Oil major: 70% of crude can be left in the ground'. Available at: https://oilprice.com/Energy/Crude-Oil/Oil-Major-70-Of-Crude-Can-Be-Left-In-The-Ground.html (accessed 1 March 2018).

Dale, M., Krumdieck, S. & Bodger, P. 2011. 'Net energy yield from production of conventional oil'. *Energy Policy*, 39(11): 7095–7102. doi: https://doi.org/10.1016/j.enpol.2011.08.021.

Dale, M., Krumdieck, S. & Bodger, P. 2012. 'Global energy modelling—A biophysical approach (GEMBA) Part 2: Methodology'. *Ecological Economics* 73: 158–167. doi: https://doi.org/10.1016/j.ecolecon.2011.10.028.

Daley, J. 2017. 'Major "clean coal" project in Mississippi shuts down'. Available at: https://www.smithsonianmag.com/smart-news/major-clean-coal-project-mississippi-shut-down-180963898/ (accessed 1 March 2018).

Davey, B. 2016. 'Shale euphoria: The boom and bust of sub prime oil and natural gas'. Available at: http://www.resilience.org/stories/2016-03-24/shale-euphoria-the-boom-and-bust-of-sub-prime-oil-and-natural-gas/ (accessed 1 March 2018).

Davis, W. 2009. *The wayfinders: Why ancient wisdom matters in the modern world.* Toronto: House of Anasasi Press.

Diamond, J. 1998. *Guns, germs, and steel: The fate of human societies.* London: Vintage.

DiChristopher, T. 2017. 'Global crude oil discoveries plunge to record low, and it's gonna get worse'. Available at: https://www.cnbc.com/2017/04/27/global-crude-oil-discoveries-plunge-to-record-low-and-its-gonna-get-worse.html (accessed 1 March 2018).

Eckersley, R. M. 2016. 'Is the West really the best? Modernisation and the psychosocial dynamics of human progress and development'. *Oxford Development Studies*: 1–17. doi: 10.1080/13600818.2016.1166197.

EIA. 2017. 'Tight oil expected to make up most of US oil production increase through 2040'. Available at: https://www.eia.gov/todayinenergy/detail.php?id=29932; and IEA. 2017. 'World Energy Outlook 2017'. Available at: https://www.iea.org/weo2017/ (accessed 1 March 2018).

Ekanayake, P. K. B., Moriarty, J. P. & Honnery, D. R. 2015. 'Equity and energy in global solutions to climate change'. *Energy for Sustainable Development* 26: 72–78.

Elliston, B., MacGill, I. & Diesendorf, M. 2013. 'Least cost 100% renewable electricity scenarios in the Australian National Electricity Market'. *Energy Policy* 59(0): 270–282. doi: http://dx.doi.org/10.1016/j.enpol.2013.03.038.

Elliston, B., MacGill, I. & Diesendorf, M. 2014. 'Comparing least cost scenarios for 100% renewable electricity with low emission fossil fuel scenarios in the Australian National Electricity Market'. *Renewable Energy* 66(0): 196–204. doi: http://dx.doi.org/10.1016/j.renene.2013.12.010 (accessed 1 March 2018).

Fahey, M. 2015. 'Oil prices and budgets: The OPEC countries most at risk'. Available at: https://www.cnbc.com/2015/12/03/oil-prices-and-budgetsthe-opec-countries-most-at-risk.html (accessed 1 March 2018).

Fisher, F. 2006. *Response ability: Environment, health and everyday transcendence.* Melbourne: Vista Publications.

Fleming, D. 2016. *Lean logic: A dictionary for the future and how to survive it.* White River Junction: Chelsea Green.

Floyd, J. 2014. 'Sense-making and acting for descent futures: human and cultural pathways.' *Foresight* 16(6): 586–607.

Floyd, J. & Slaughter, R. 2014. Descent pathways. *Foresight* 16(6): 485–495. doi: http://dx.doi.org/10.1108/FS-07-2014-0049 (accessed 1 March 2018).

Foeger, L. 2017. 'Oil price collapse cost OPEC countries over $1tn'. Available at: https://www.rt.com/business/406820-opec-oil-prices-collapse-losses/ (accessed 1 March 2018).

Friedmann, A. 2016. *When the trucks stop running: Energy and the future of transportation.* New York: Springer.

Fustier, K., Gray, G., Gundersen, C. & Hilboldt, T. 2016. 'Global oil supply: Will mature field declines drive the next supply crunch?' HSBC Global Research Report (September 2016). Available at: https://drive.google.com/file/d/oB9wSgViWVAfzUEgzMIBfR3UxNDg/view (accessed 1 March 2018).

Geden, O. 2018. 'Politically informed advice for climate action'. *Nature Geoscience.* doi: 10.1038/s41561-018-0143-3.

Gosden, E. 2016. 'Oil demand peak "not in sight" as stage set for boom and bust, says IEA'. Available at: http://www.telegraph.co.uk/business/2016/11/16/oil-demand-peak-not-in-sight-as-stage-set-for-boom-and-bust-says/ (accessed 1 March 2018).

Gosden, E. 2016. 'Oil supply crunch "to hit in 2019" as investment in new projects dries up'. Available at: http://www.telegraph.co.uk/business/2016/11/22/oil-supply-crunch-hit-2019-investment-new-projects-dries/ (accessed 1 March 2018).

Greer, J. M. 2008. *The long descent: A user's guide to the end of the industrial age.* Gabriola Island, Canada: New Society Publishers.

Greer, J. M. 2009. *The ecotechnic future: Envisioning a post-peak world.* Gabriola Island, Canada: New Society Publishers.

Greer, J. M. 2011. *The wealth of nature: Economics as if survival mattered.* Gabriola Island, Canada: New Society Publishers.

Hall, C. A. S. 2017. *Energy return on investment: A unifying principle for biology, economics, and sustainability*: New York: Springer.

Hall, C. A. S. & Klitgaard, K. A. 2011. *Energy and the wealth of nations: Understanding the biophysical economy.* New York: Springer.

Hamilton, C. 2014. *Earthmasters: The dawn of the age of climate engineering.* New Haven: Yale University Press.

Hamilton, J. 2011. 'Historical oil shocks'. Available at: http://econweb.ucsd.edu/ ~jhamilton/oil_history.pdf (accessed 1 March 2018).

Hamilton, J. 2012. 'Oil prices, exhaustible resources, and economic growth' (NBER working paper 17759). Available at: http://www.nber.org/papers/w17759.pdf (accessed 1 March 2018).

Hausfather, Z. 2018. 'How much "carbon budget" is left to limit global warming to 1.5C?' *Ecologise.in.* (18 April). Available at: https://www.ecologise.in/2018/04/18/how-much-carbon-budget-is-left-to-limit-global-warming-to-1-5c/ (accessed 2 July 2018).

Heinberg, R. & Fridley, D. 2016. *Our renewable future: Laying the path for one hundred percent clean energy.* Washington: Island Press. Available at: http:// ourrenewablefuture.org/#the-book (accessed 1 March 2018).

Heinberg, R. 2018. 'New US record-Level oil production! Peak oil theory disproven! Not.' Available at: http://www.resilience.org/stories/2018-03-06/new-u-s-record-level-oil-production-peak-oil-theory-disproven-not/ (accessed 19 June 2018).

Helal, Y. 2016. 'More spending cuts as UAE predicts oil shortages'. Available at: http:// www.arabianindustry.com/oil-gas/news/2016/nov/6/more-spending-cuts-as-uae-predicts-oil-shortages-5531344/ (accessed 1 March 2018).

Hiltzik, M. 2017. 'A Stanford professor didn't just debate his scientific critics—he sued them for $10 million'. Available at: http://www.latimes.com/business/hiltzik/la-fi-hiltzik-jacobson-lawsuit-20171121-story.html (accessed 1 March 2018).

Hirsch, R. 2007. 'Peaking of world oil production: Recent forecasts' (DOE/NETL-20017/1263): 13. Available at: https://netl.doe.gov/File%20Library/Research/ Energy%20Analysis/Publications/DOE-NETL-2007-1263-PeakingWorldOilProd-RecentForecasts.pdf (accessed 1 March 2018).

Hirsch, R. 2012. 'Peak Oil: Some knowns and unknowns'. *ASPOUSA* presentation (December 2012). Available at: https://www.youtube.com/watch?v=PVoDYha8ZRM (accessed 20 August 2018).

Hirth, L. 2013. 'The market value of variable renewables: The effect of solar and wind power variability on their relative price'. *Energy economics* 38: 218–236.

Holmgren, D. 2009. *Future scenarios: Mapping the cultural implications of peak oil and climate change.* Available at: http://www.futurescenarios.org/ (accessed 1 March 2018).

Homer-Dixon, T. 2007. *The upside of down: Catastrophe, creativity, and the renewal of civilization*. Melbourne: Text Publishing.

Hughes, D. 2018. 'Shale reality check: Drilling into the U.S. government's rosy projections for shale and gas oil production through 2050.' *Post Carbon Institute Report* (4 February 2018). Available at: https://www.postcarbon.org/publications/shale-reality-check/# (accessed 20 August 2018).

Husain, A. et al. 2015. 'Global implications of lower oil prices' (SDN/15/15). Available at: https://www.imf.org/external/pubs/ft/sdn/2015/sdn1515.pdf (accessed 1 March 2018).

Illich, I. 1974. *Energy and Equity* (Vol. 45). New York: Harper & Row.

International Energy Agency. 2016. 'Global oil discoveries and new projects fell to historic lows in 2016'. Available at: https://www.iea.org/newsroom/news/2017/april/global-oil-discoveries-and-new-projects-fell-to-historic-lows-in-2016.html (accessed 1 March 2018).

International Energy Agency. 2017a. 'World Energy Outlook 2017: Executive Summary'. Available at: https://www.iea.org/Textbase/npsum/weo2017SUM.pdf (accessed 28 February 2018).

International Energy Agency, 2017b. No title. Presentation at launch event for the World Energy Outlook 2017. Available at: https://www.facebook.com/internationalenergyagency/videos/10157417220717228/ (accessed 20 August 2018).

Ison, R. 2010. *Systems practice: How to act in a climate-change world*. London: Springer.

Jackson, T. 2009. *Prosperity without growth: Economics for a finite planet*. London: Earthscan.

Jacobson, M. et al. 2017. '100% clean and renewable wind, water, and sunlight all-sector energy roadmaps for 139 countries of the world'. *Joule* 1: 108–121.

Jordan, A. et al. 2013. 'Going beyond two degrees? The risks and opportunities of alternative options'. *Climate Policy* 13(6): 751–769.

Kalimeris, P., Richardson, C. & Bithas, K. 2014. 'A meta-analysis investigation of the direction of the energy-GDP causal relationship: Implications for the growth-degrowth dialogue'. *Journal of Cleaner Production* 67: 1–13.

Keen, S. 2011. *Debunking economics: The naked emperor of the social sciences*. 2nd edn. London: Zed Books.

Kharecha, P. & Hansen, J. 2008. 'Implications of "peak oil" for atmospheric CO_2 and climate'. Available at: https://arxiv.org/ftp/arxiv/papers/0704/0704.2782.pdf (accessed 1 March 2018).

King, A., Karoly, D. & Henley, B. 2017. 'Australian climate extremes at 1.5C and 2C of global warming', *Nature Climate Change* 7:412-416.

Kopits, S. 2014. 'Oil and economic growth: A supply-constrained view' (11 February 2014). Available at: http://energypolicy.columbia.edu/sites/default/files/Kopits%20-%20Oil%20and%20Economic%20Growth%20(SIPA,%202014)%20-%20Presentation%20Version%5B1%5D.pdf (accessed 1 March 2018).

Krumdieck, S. 2013. 'Transition engineering: Adaptation of complex systems for survival'. *International Journal of Sustainable Development* 16(3/4): 310–321.

Krumdieck, S. & Page, S. 2013. 'Retro-analysis of liquid bio-ethanol and bio-diesel in New Zealand'. *Energy Policy* 62: 363–371. doi: https://doi.org/10.1016/j.enpol.2013.07.078.

Krumdieck, S., Dale, M. & Page, S. 2012. 'Design and implementation of a community based sustainable development action research method'. *Social Business* 2(4): 291–337. doi: 10.1362/204440812x13546197293131.

Lenzen, M., McBain, B., Trainer, T., Jütte, S., Rey-Lescure, O. & Huang, J. 2016. 'Simulating low-carbon electricity supply for Australia'. *Applied Energy* 179: 553–564. doi: http://dx.doi.org/10.1016/j.apenergy.2016.06.151 (accessed 1 March 2018).

Locatelli, G., Mancini, M. & Todeschini, N. 2013. 'Generation IV nuclear reactors: Current status and future prospects'. *Energy Policy* 61: 1503–1520. doi: https://doi.org/10.1016/j.enpol.2013.06.101.

McArdle, P. 2018. Various articles tagged 'wind diversity'. *Watt Clarity*. Available at: http://www.wattclarity.com.au/tag/wind-diversity/ (accessed 20 August 2018).

McGlade, C. & Ekins, P. 2015. 'The geographical distribution of fossil fuels unused when limiting global warming to 2 degrees'. *Nature* 517: 187–190. Available at: https://www.nature.com/articles/nature14016 (accessed 1 March 2018).

Meadows, D., Randers, J. & Meadows, D. 2005. *Limits to growth: The 30-year update*. London: Earthscan.

Mearns, E. 2015. 'The wind in Spain blows.' *Energy Matters* (30 November). Available at: http://euanmearns.com/the-wind-in-spain-blows/ (accessed 20 August 2018).

Miller, L. M., Brunsell, N. A., Mechem, D. B., Gans, F., Monaghan, A. J., Vautard, R., Keith, D. W. & Kleidon, A. 2015. 'Two methods for estimating limits to large-scale wind power generation'. *Proceedings of the National Academy of Sciences* 112(36): 11169–11174. doi: 10.1073/pnas.1408251112.

Miller, L. M., Gans, F. & Kleidon, A. 2011. 'Estimating maximum global land surface wind power extractability and associated climatic consequences'. *Earth System Dynamics* 2(1): 1–12. Doi: http://dx.doi.org/10.5194/esd-2-1-2011 (accessed 1 March 2018).

Miller, R. & Sorrel, S. 2014. 'The future of oil supply'. *Phil. Trans. of the Royal Society A*372, 20130179: 6.

Mohr, S. et al. 2015. 'Projection of world fossil fuels by country'. *Fuel* 141: 120–35.

Montgomery, J. B. & O'Sullivan, F. M. 2017. 'Spatial variability of tight oil well productivity and the impact of technology'. *Applied Energy* 195: 344–355.

Moriarty, P. & Honnery, D. 2011. *Rise and Fall of the Carbon Civilisation*. London: Springer.

Moriarty, P. & Honnery, D. 2012. 'Preparing for a low-energy future'. *Futures* 44(10): 883–892.

Moriarty, P. & Honnery, D. 2016. 'Can renewable energy power the future?' *Energy Policy* 93: 3–7.

Mumford, L. 1966. *The myth of the machine: Technics and human development.* New York: Harcourt Brace.

Mumford, L. 2010. *Technics and civilization.* Chicago: University of Chicago Press.

Murphy, D. 2014. 'The implications of the declining energy return on investment of oil production'. *Phil. Trans. of the Royal Society A.* 372(2006). Available at: http://rsta. royalsocietypublishing.org/content/372/2006/20130126 (accessed 1 March 2018).

Murphy, D. & Hall, C. 2011. Energy return on investment, peak oil, and the end of economic growth. *Annals of the New York Academy of Sciences*, 1219(1), 52–72. doi: 10.1111/j.1749-6632.2010.05940.x: 52.

Murphy, T. 2011. 'The energy trap'. *Do the Math.* (18 October). Available at: https:// dothemath.ucsd.edu/2011/10/the-energy-trap/ (accessed 4 October 2018).

Mushalik, M. 2016. 'World outside US and Canada doesn't produce more crude oil than in 2005'. *Crude oil peak.* Available at: http://crudeoilpeak.info/world-outside-us-and-canada-doesnt-produce-more-crude-oil-than-in-2005 (accessed 1 March 2018).

NASA. 'Long-term warming trend continued in 2017: NASA, NOAA.' Available at: https://www.nasa.gov/press-release/long-term-warming-trend-continued-in-2017-nasa-noaa (accessed 28 February 2018).

Neslen, A. 2016. 'Europe's oil imports "dependent on unstable countries"'. Available at: https://www.theguardian.com/environment/2016/jul/12/europes-oil-imports-dependent-on-unstable-countries (accessed 1 March 2018).

Olson, B. & Cook, L. 2017. 'US shale juggernaut shows sign of fatigue'. Available at: https://www.wsj.com/articles/u-s-shale-juggernaut-shows-signs-of-fatigue-1507195802 (accessed 1 March 2018).

Olson, B. & Cook, L. 2017. 'Wall Street tells frackers to stop counting barrels, start making profits'. Available at: https://www.wsj.com/articles/wall-streets-fracking-frenzy-runs-dry-as-profits-fail-to-materialize-1512577420 (accessed 1 March 2018).

Oyedele, A. 2017. 'Oil discoveries are at an all-time low—and the clock is clicking'. Available at: http://www.businessinsider.com/oil-discoveries-fall-to-lowest-since-1940s-2017-12/?r=AU&IR=T (accessed 1 March 2018).

Palmer, G. 2014. *Energy in Australia: Peak oil, solar power, and Asia's economic growth.* New York: Springer.

Palmer, G. 2018. 'A biophysical perspective of IPCC integrated energy modelling'. *Energies* 11(4): 839. doi: https://doi.org/10.3390/en11040839 (accessed 1 March 2018).

Palmer, G. & Floyd, J. 2017. 'An exploration of divergence in EPBT and EROI for solar photovoltaics'. *BioPhysical Economics and Resource Quality* 2(4): 1–20. doi: 10.1007/s41247-017-0033-0.

Paraskova, T. 2017. 'US shale's most productive play may peak by 2021'. Available at: https://oilprice.com/Energy/Crude-Oil/US-Shales-Most-Productive-Play-May-Peak-By-2021.html (accessed 1 March 2018).

'Paris Agreement, The', 2015. Available at: https://unfccc.int/files/meetings/paris_nov_2015/application/pdf/paris_agreement_english_.pdf (accessed 1 March 2018).

Patterson, R. 2014. 'World crude oil exports'. Available at: http://peakoilbarrel.com/world-crude-oil-exports/ (accessed 1 March 2018).

Patterson, R. 2017. 'US shale could peak before 2025'. Available at: https://oilprice.com/Energy/Energy-General/US-Shale-Could-Peak-Before-2025.html (accessed 1 March 2018).

Pearce, J. M. 2008. 'Thermodynamic limitations to nuclear energy deployment as a greenhouse gas mitigation technology'. *Int. J. of Nuclear Governance, Economy and Ecology*, 2(1): 113–130. http://www.inderscience.com/offer.php?id=17358 (accessed 1 March 2018).

Peters, G. & Geden, O. 2017. 'Catalysing a political shift from low to negative carbon'. *Nature Climate Change* 7: 619–621. Available at: https://www.nature.com/articles/nclimate3369 (accessed 1 March 2018).

Peters, G. P. 2018. 'Beyond carbon budgets'. *Nature Geoscience* 11(6): 378–380. doi: 10.1038/s41561-018-0142-4.

Piketty, T. 2014. *Capital in the twenty-first century* (A. Goldhammer, Trans.). Cambridge, Massachusetts: Harvard University Press.

Pilkey, O. H. & Pilkey-Jarvis, L. 2007. *Useless arithmetic: Why environmental scientists can't predict the future*. New York: Columbia University Press.

Pollard, S. 1968. *The idea of progress: History and society*. London: C. A. Watts.

Polson, J. & Loh, T. 2017. 'US vastly overestimates oil output forecasts, MIT study suggests'. Available at: https://www.bloomberg.com/news/articles/2017-12-01/mit-study-suggests-u-s-vastly-overstates-oil-output-forecasts (accessed 1 March 2018).

Rabinowitz, A. 2017. 'The dirty secret of the world's plan to avert climate disaster'. Available at: https://www.wired.com/story/the-dirty-secret-of-the-worlds-plan-to-avert-climate-disaster/ (accessed 1 March 2018).

Rapier, R. 2017. 'Peak oil demand is millions of barrels away'. Available at: https://www.forbes.com/sites/rrapier/2017/06/19/peak-oil-demand-is-millions-of-barrels-away/#38c0a10f6940 (accessed 1 March 2018).

Raworth, K. 2017. *Doughnut economics: Seven ways to think like a 21st-century economist*. London: Random House.

Rogelj, L. et al. 2015. 'Energy system transformations for limiting end-of-century warming to below 1.5C'. *Nature Climate Change* 5: 519–526.

Roszak, T. 1972. *Where the wasteland ends: Politics and transcendence in postindustrial society*: New York: Doubleday.

Sahlins, M. 1972. *Stone age economics*. Chicago: Aldine.

Schaps, K. & Dolan, D. 2017. 'Aramco CEO sees oil supply shortage as investments, discoveries drop'. Available at: https://www.reuters.com/article/us-aramco-oil/aramco-ceo-sees-oil-supply-shortage-as-investments-discoveries-drop-idUSKBN19V0KR (accessed 1 March 2018).

Scheyder, E. & McWilliams, G. 2017. 'Oil majors still years from repairing balance sheets after price war'. Available at: https://www.reuters.com/article/us-ceraweek-spending/oil-majors-still-years-from-repairing-balance-sheets-after-price-war-idUSKBN16F27F (accessed 1 March 2018).

Schumacher, E. F. 1973. *Small is beautiful: Economics as if people mattered*. London: Blond and Briggs.

Sgouridis, S., Csala, D. & Bardi, U. 2016. 'The sower's way: Quantifying the narrowing net-energy pathways to a global energy transition'. *Environmental Research Letters* 11(9): 094009.

Shahine, A. & Khraiche, D. 2017. 'Oil cuts add to Saudi pain as GDP contracts for second quarter'. Available at: https://www.bloomberg.com/news/articles/2017-09-30/saudi-gdp-shrinks-for-second-quarter-in-a-row-amid-opec-cuts (accessed 1 March 2018).

Slaughter, R. A. 2010. *The biggest wake up call in history*. Indooroopilly, Queensland: Foresight International.

Smil, V. 1994. *Energy in world history*. Boulder: Westview Press.

Smil, V. 2010. *Energy transitions: History, requirements, and prospects*. Santa Barbara: Prager Publishers.

Smil, V. 2015. *Power density: Key to understanding energy sources and uses*. Cambridge: MIT Press.

Spratt, D. & Dunlop, I. 2017. 'What lies beneath: The scientific understatement of climate risks'. Breakthrough Institute: 15. Available at: https://docs.wixstatic.com/ugd/148cb0_56b252a7d78b485badde2fadcba88d00.pdf (accessed 1 March 2018).

Spratt, D. 2014. 'The real budgetary emergency and the myth of "burnable carbon". *Climate Code Red* (22 May). Available at: http://www.climatecodered.org/2014/05/the-real-budgetary-emergency-burnable.html (accessed 1 March 2018).

Spratt, D. 2016. 'Unravelling the myth of a "carbon budget" for 1.5C'. Available at: http://www.climatecodered.org/2016/09/unravelling-myth-of-carbon-budget-for.html (accessed 1 March 2018).

Spratt, D. 2017. 'Paris 1.5–2C target far from safe, say world-leading scientists'. Available at: http://reneweconomy.com.au/paris-1-5-2c-target-far-from-safe-say-world-leading-scientists-81532/ (accessed 1 March 2018).

Stafford, J. 2017. 'The IEA is grossly overestimating shale growth'. Available at: https://oilprice.com/Energy/Oil-Prices/The-IEA-Is-Grossly-Overestimating-Shale-Growth.html (accessed 1 March 2018).

Stern, N. 2007. 'Stern Review: The economics of climate change'. Available at: http://mudancasclimaticas.cptec.inpe.br/~rmclima/pdfs/destaques/sternreview_report_complete.pdf (accessed 1 March 2018).

Tainter, J. 1988. *The collapse of complex societies*. Cambridge: Cambridge University Press.

Tainter, J. 2006. 'Social complexity and sustainability'. *Ecological complexity* 3: 91–103.

Tainter, J. A. 2011. 'Energy, complexity, and sustainability: A historical perspective'. *Environmental Innovation and Societal Transitions* 1(1): 89–95. doi: http://dx.doi.org/10.1016/j.eist.2010.12.001 (accessed 1 March 2018).

Tainter, J. A. & Patzek, T. W. 2012. *Drilling down: The gulf oil debacle and our energy dilemma*. New York: Copernicus.

Thompson, H. 2017. *Oil and the Western economic crisis*. London: Palgrave Macmillan.

Trainer, T. 2010. *The transition to a sustainable and just world*. Sydney: Envirobook.

Trainer, T. 2017. 'Some problems in storing renewable energy'. *Energy Policy* 110 (Supplement C): 386–393. doi: https://doi.org/10.1016/j.enpol.2017.07.061 (accessed 1 March 2018).

Turner, G. M. 2012. 'On the cusp of global collapse? Updated comparison of The Limits to Growth with historical data'. *GAIA-Ecological Perspectives for Science and Society* 21(2): 116–124.

Tverberg, G. 2012. 'Oil supply limits and the continuing financial crisis'. *Energy* 37(1): 27–34.

Van den Bergh, J., Folke, C., Polasky, S. Scheffer, M. & Steffan, W. 2015. 'What if solar energy becomes really cheap? A thought experiment on environmental problem shifting'. *Environmental Sustainability* 14: 170–179. doi: https://doi.org/10.1016/j.cosust.2015.05.007.

Vaughan, N. & Gough, C. (2016). 'Expert assessment concludes negative emissions scenarios may not deliver. *Environmental Research Letters* 11(9): 095003. doi:10.1088/1748-9326/11/9/095003.

Zhang, Z. et al. 2016. 'The Shandong Shidao Bay 200 MWe high-temperature gas-cooled reactor pebble-bed module (HTR-PM) demonstration power plant: An engineering and technological innovation'. *Engineering* 2(1): 112–118. doi: https://doi.org/10.1016/J.ENG.2016.01.020 (accessed 1 March 2018).

Index

Made in the USA
Columbia, SC
14 October 2018